'The more I learn about people, the more I like my dog'

Mark Twain

Sit, Stay, Roll Over
Rolo the Border Terrier's Guide to Training your Humans

Quill and Apple Publishing

Quill and Apple Publishing
First Published in 2017
Mayfield
East Sussex

A CIP catalogue record for this book is available from the British Library

Print ISBN 978-0-9935775-2-9
E Pub ISBN 978-0-9935775-3-6

Illustrations by Sally C Greenfield
Printed and bound in Great Britain by Print2Demand, 17 Burgess Road, Hastings, East Sussex, TN35 4NR.

Preface

Ears Pricked.....

Dogs and humans are meant to be together. They have a relationship that goes way back into the distant past that was based on a shared preoccupation with food and sourcing the next meal. Not much has changed there then. However, the world has altered around us and people no longer have to hunt wild boar using spears, with a faithful canine snapping at its heels. Instead they just trundle to the local supermarket and buy it segmented, shrink wrapped and sanitised, whilst their pooch waits patiently, with snapping of any kind definitely forbidden.

And that's at the heart of the matter for your modern dog; the relationship has changed rapidly and humankind has struggled to keep up. There are misunderstandings and problems of all kinds that stem back to a fundamental lack of comprehension and poor communication.

1

So I'm a dog on a mission to breach that void. I'm a senior Border Terrier who's been down the lane and round the block a few times, so I've got a wealth of experience to draw upon. Whilst I still have the occasional problem with my family, who I refer to as 'Them Indoors' to protect their anonymity, I've largely got them where I want them, although 'Him Indoors' who never wanted a dog in the first place – unsanitary creatures with disreputable personal habits that shed fur, cost money and pong a bit – is still a work in progress.

I've already got my own blog[1], and unusually for a dog that normally barks, tweet as @stockton_rolo. I write a monthly column for Magnet magazine and I've also written a previous book, *The Last Rolo*. However, I felt that some more specific guidance was called for, hence my training manual. Whether you're a young pup just starting out or an older dog that's run into a few issues with their family, this is for you. However, the book does come with one significant caveat: don't show it to your humans. We dogs need to keep our cards close to our chests and maintain the correct balance of power in order for the relationship to work. We certainly don't want them understanding us; that would never do. After all, it's that little bit of mystery that keeps us interesting. So, assuming you are alone and the coast is clear, relax in your dog bed, pay attention, and let's start right at the beginning...

---

[1] www.rolotheborderterrier.blogspot.com

Chapter One

Starting Out

If you are a young pup, just about to launch yourself into the outside world, then there are some first big decisions that are critical to your health and well-being for the rest of your life. No pressure there then!

If you're an older dog, you might be in the unfortunate position of making these choices for the second or even third time around. It could be that you just made some mistakes first time, or it might be that you've been unlucky and that although you made sound choices at the time, circumstances have changed and, through no fault of your own, you are having to re-consider. Either way, here's some advice that will help you to make the right decisions about your owner, your family, your home and your support services.

Choosing Your Owner

Before you start on the critical task of choosing an owner, you need to try and set aside your amiable canine instinct to like everyone, and no matter how appealing their eyes, how adoring their language, or how big the treats, you must be rational and objective. Many a pup has come unstuck by seeing only the positive in people rather than apprising them critically, weighing up both their merits and deficiencies. You must also be wary of being influenced in your judgment of people by the beguiling "Oh, he's sooo cuuute" especially if you're a 'she', and when accompanied by ear caressing and tummy rubs. Instead you must put your paw down firmly from the outset and consider all the pertinent factors.

A common misconception is that you can have more than one owner. Every dog has a different relationship with various members of their family but there will be one person who feeds you, usually accompanies you on your walks, picks up your little offerings, clears up after any unfortunate mishaps, tends to you in your sick bed, and who is the focus for your particular training. This person is your owner and needs to be selected with especial care.

Firstly, there needs to be a degree of self-honesty. What kind of pooch are you? Are you an affable gun dog who is eager to please but who needs plenty of exercise? Perhaps you're a lap dog who likes a bit of pampering and a dainty cuisine. Or maybe you are an independent minded terrier with a strong hunting instinct and less than innocent preoccupation with small furry creatures. You could be a cross-breed in which case you need to consider your family tree as more than just a convenient weeing post. We dogs come in lots of different shapes and sizes with very differing requirements so you need to make sure that these match up with your intended human.

And owners come in lots of different shapes and sizes too. As with dogs, choosing a particular type is no absolute guarantee, but there are various categories that potential owners fall into and you should be fully aware of what type you are faced with before making your choice.

The couch potato – They can be of either gender and any age, although the middle years predominate in owners of this type. They are often over-weight as they are not very keen on exercise, although, confusingly for a young dog, they frequently wear sports gear because it has got elasticated waistbands. They prefer to sit on a nice comfy sofa in the warm and dry, ideally with a cup or glass of something and a little snack. They enjoy watching TV, spending hours on social media, playing computer games and chatting on their phones. If you are a dog who is not going to require a great deal of exercise, is happy lounging around sharing snacks and has good techniques for attracting attention when your owner is distracted by screen action, then this type might be worth considering.

The fitness fanatic – Again, age and gender are not necessarily indicators, but they can often be seen wearing Lycra, which quite frankly ought to be government licensed, or good quality outdoor wear with proper walking boots and a coat of the type that needs reproofing. They will eat healthy foods and have a list of things they don't include in their diet longer than the list of things that they do. They will drink concoctions of dubious shades out of blenders, and will be abstemious in the treats and beverages department. If you're a dog who needs a lot of exercise or perhaps have some allergies or food intolerances then this type of owner would be ideal.

The carer – At first glance this would seem the obvious choice for almost any kind of dog. After all, they are the sort of person who spends their life running around after others. They are often, but not exclusively, female and are usually aged thirty-five plus. They can be identified by their practical clothing which sometimes looks as if it's been put on in a hurry, and often has little hints of the owner's daily preoccupations such as baby food, paint, play dough and food stains. Now this kind of owner has some serious advantages in the accidental treats and clearing up after you department, but you need to be a dog who can survive the hurly-burly of everyday family life. You also need to like people in general and juniors in particular, which is why breeds such as Labradors and Golden Retrievers often pick this type of owner.

The fashionable owner – This title tends to suggest they'd be the ideal companion for the toy breeds who don't mind being picked up and carried and will tolerate bows in their fur and wearing little coats and outfits which generally make them look like a complete t**! However, it also covers the kind of owner who has the matching Range Rover, Aga and wellie boots and would suit gundog breeds or fashionable crosses which invariably involve Poo, not of the kind that needs picking up in little bags. Appearance is everything here so you need to make sure that your owner is a good match and really appreciates the unique qualities you bring to the relationship.

The competitive owner – If you choose this kind of owner you need to have some star qualities or potential to develop them. They will appreciate your close match to your breed standard, not objecting to complete strangers feeling you all over, peering at your teeth and checking your genitals, and your preparedness for trotting around a ring happily whilst they strut their stuff. Alternatively, your owner needs to be in complete harmony with you so that you understand each other instinctively and can compete in obedience, or, if you have a particularly fey disposition, heelwork to music. There are some interesting variations: agility for the agile owner or flyball for the fast, so you need to make sure that your particular owner has the necessary qualities to keep up.

Empty nesters – These often make good owners. Their children will have grown-up and will either have left home or be shortly at the point of doing so and they can bestow their love, affection and time on you instead. You can usually expect them to be very diligent in exercising, after all they'll be middle-aged or senior and will be trying to keep their weight down and attempting to maintain some degree of fitness. They do have one or two disadvantages in that they've been round the block a few times so are not easily fooled. They also tend to take long holidays which may or may not include you. And finally, if they are female, beware of the knitting needles, you never know what they may make you, although it's not so bad if they're into baking and it's edible.

Child substitute owners – If you are the kind of dog that likes to be the centre of attention and isn't that fussed on juniors then this type of owner can be a good choice. These are usually, but not always, part of a couple, who have decided against or can't have children, and you will be fulfilling their need to have something to love and care for. They are very attentive owners so if you are the kind of dog that needs some personal space then they might not be the one for you.

Tough owners – You must be careful choosing this kind of owner. You don't want someone whose disposition or upbringing has made them inclined to nastiness. It used to be that this type was predominantly male, with tattoos, piercings and a shaven head, although female versions are available, but these features have become increasingly common in the general population so it can be a bit tricky to distinguish them. If you want to look tough, then this is the type of owner for you. They will match your studded collar and swaggering gait. They are often chosen by breeds with a history of fighting or guarding such as Bull Terriers, Mastiffs, Rottweilers or German Shepherds, although the best of this type of owner are actually big softies at heart – it's all bluster.

The well-to-do owner – These are owners who have stacks of money, or an aristocratic pedigree; ideally both. They are usually well–dressed in classic but expensive brands, and have large houses and gardens making them the ideal choice for the giant breeds such as Great Danes and Irish Wolfhounds who have size issues. Oddly enough, they are sometimes a good choice for scruffy mongrels as these owners are not trying to prove anything – they've already got it.

So there you have it. It's not a definitive list by any means but it does give you a rough idea. Give some careful thought to the type or types of owner that would suit you; it's best to have done your homework before you meet so that you won't be swayed by emotion. After all, remember, an owner is for life, not just for Christmas.

Choosing Your Family

It might be that your owner is single, which can be a worry as they might acquire a partner along the way and although you should be invited to express your view, occasionally an inconsiderate, badly trained owner acquires a new companion without an appropriate level of consultation, which can lead to problems.

Couples

If your new owner has a partner, you need to consider carefully the nature of that relationship. Have they been together long? Do they generally get on? Many a pooch has run into difficulties when a couple split up and you don't want to be involved in a costly and emotionally draining custody battle to ensure you retain the correct person. In the time that it takes to select an owner, it might be difficult to fully ascertain the nature of their relationship, but if they arrive not speaking because someone has contradicted the sat nav and sent them the wrong way down a one-way street, then be cautious, they may not be the owner for you.

Another consideration is whether or not they are of breeding age. If so, don't be deceived by pronouncements that they don't want children, after all 'Him Indoors' once said he didn't want a dog....

Families

These are often the ideal choice for an out-going, friendly dog and give you the opportunity to train the next generation of dog-lovers. However, you need to ensure that the children know how to behave otherwise there may be difficulties. Again, it can be difficult to assess in the time that you've got but if they are bouncing on the sofas, throwing tantrums, or even worse, toys, without any sign of an effective check by their parents, then beware.

Also, make sure in that first meeting that you bestow your affections equally around the family. You won't know at this stage the various dispositions and pecking order. Sometimes the males can appear to be in charge, but it is often the females that really rule the roost. Also the juniors, as is the case with my own 'Junior Her', can carry a lot of clout. After all it is 'Junior Her' in our family who is the most besotted dog-lover, and finds merit in even the most unlikely of canines. Even if they're downright ugly, they're 'cute', and she has always been an unfailing champion in my all-too-frequent moments of crisis. She is followed closely in the dog-loving stakes by 'Her Indoors'. Even now, despite my training, 'Her Indoors' makes an unseemly fuss of pretty much any canine she meets, and heaven help us if we meet a puppy.

Years of effort on my behalf goes out of the window instantly. Still, you can only do your best...

Choosing Your Home
Now this can be rather tricky as it is almost impossible to know, when viewing your family, what kind of home they have, although you might be able to pick up a few clues from their conversation and appearance. To be honest, canine requirements are pretty basic. It doesn't have to be tidy, or even especially clean, but it does need to be warm and dry with easy access to some outside space. In fact, the type of home that can be the most difficult is the fastidiously clean and tidy type, where dog hair, muddy footprints and droplets shaken from wet coats are going to instantly show up and cause affront. 'Her Indoors' has worrying tendencies in that direction so I have to endure constantly washed floors and bedding. 'Him Indoors' is even worse as he extends his fixation with an orderly and pristine environment to me. Any sign that I've become wiffy, which is a subjective appraisal at the best of times, and I'm whisked off into the baby bath and lathered up with tea tree oil shampoo, which leaves me smelling like a French Poodle for days. Still, I guess if I'd been a French Poodle, that wouldn't have been a problem, which takes my right back to my fundamental point: the importance of compatibility between dog and owner.

How to Make Your Choice
One of the questions, as a dog of some experience, that I'm often asked by anxious pups, is how you go about choosing your owner. This is really rather simple. All

prospective owners will have done a bit of research and will know to avoid puppies who are listless, ill, undersized or grumpy, so if you don't like the look of them or don't think they are right for you, the course is clear. Size is a difficult one, particularly if like me, you're keen on your food, but sucking your tummy in and cringing a bit, can create the impression of smallness, even if the reality is rather different. Listless is easy. Just lie by yourself and refuse to join in. If they try and pick you up run and cower behind your mother or siblings. If things get really desperate try a bit of puppy growling when they come near you, or see if you can bring up some of your tea – that should sort it.

If you are an older dog looking for a new home, then the same principles apply although you need to be careful you don't overdo it in the growling department. Try demonstrating some aggression towards an inanimate object like a bowl, toy or basket. Your 'ill-health' card will need to be a bit more subtle. Try scratching a lot, drinking water like it's suddenly going on ration, twitching and, best of all, going cross-eyed! This is easy to achieve – just stare at the end of your nose, unless of course you are a Pug, in which case you'll just have to improvise.

When you've found the right owner, go for it big time! You don't want to run the risk of missing out. Be lively, engaging, friendly, cute; it hardly needs saying. Once you've got the right person, the rest is relatively plain sailing.

Choosing Your Support Services

The idea that your owner and family can consistently meet all your needs is, quite frankly, old-fashioned. With the pace of modern life you are likely to need a range of support services and it is important that you get these right, from the outset.

Alternative Care Providers

We dogs are companionable animals, and there will be times when no-one is at home. It is not a good idea to regularly allow your owner to be apart from you for long periods of time. They can develop bad habits such as a fixation with work, inappropriate alcohol consumption and a worrying tendency to fill their free time with distraction activities which can be of varying types but come under the generic heading of 'hobbies'. You should be firm about all of these from the outset. After all, jobs, although vital for mental stimulation, social interaction and money for your toys, food, vet bills and treats, do not love them back. If there's any alcohol consumption going on, why are you not involved? There are plenty of pubs that allow dogs and the odd drop from the bottom of a beer bottle never did anyone any harm, although that time I drank all the beer from the slug traps in the garden and the ensuing hangover, was perhaps taking things a bit too far. And as for hobbies, there are plenty that can involve you: walking, running, bike and horse riding, gardening, dog shows, caravanning and camping, the list is extensive.

However, even with the best trained of owners, there will be times when life gets in the way and you will have to be apart, so you will need to consider who you would like to look after you.

Grandparents – Depending on the age of your owner, and whether or not they are available, local, and up to the task, these make excellent care providers. As your owners are clearly dog-lovers, they have probably been first trained in that amiable instinct, by their own parents. Also, grandparents have an innate 'spoiling' disposition that they extend to their grandchildren if they have any, so they have already been trained in the basics of treat giving and are lavish with their affections. They are also less likely to be overly fussy about their domestic environment as they have a more measured view of life, honed by years of experience. The only things to be wary of are an old-fashioned tendency, amongst a small minority, to view corporal punishment as acceptable for dogs, which of course, can never be right. They are also usually rather canny, which can be a disadvantage for the more adventurous dog as they tend to anticipate and prevent little escapades when they are still in the planning stages, which can be frustrating.

I've been particularly blessed with my grandparents. 'Her Indoors' Mum and Dad are both lifelong dog lovers, who have a holiday home abroad which prevents them from being owned by their own dog. They are however, always genuinely pleased to see me, give me free range of the house and garden, and positively encourage me to do certain things like chase and bark at pigeons and cats, which I'm actively discouraged from doing at home. They are also patient in the playing with me, tummy rubs and ear tickling departments.

'Him Indoors' mother has never had a dog of her own but that hasn't stopped her from responding very well to training and lavishing me with treats, presents and affection. She also has a pleasing tendency to see things from my point of view, something that 'Junior Her' has inherited, and which is a very useful trait.

Friends and neighbours – These have the advantage of caring for you in your own home, but generally it is only fair to use them for occasional situations as you don't want them feeling that they're being taken advantage of. They ideally need to be dog owners, or to have previously owned a dog themselves, although that isn't an absolute rule. One of the best occasional carers I have is a friend of 'Her Indoors' called Danielle, who's never owned a dog. She does however have a strong sense of mischief and fun, plus a soft heart that has been easily trained to respond to my 'hungry eyes'. On one recent occasion, having looked after me previously in the late afternoon or early evening when she had been left instructions to give me my tea, she was given a lunch time shift. Not being a dog owner, and confused by the absence of feeding instructions, she assumed that we dogs have three meals a day like people, and gave me a substantial lunch. I didn't let on and when 'Them Indoors' came back from their outing, I happily munched my way through my evening repast as well. They didn't find out about my additional meal until it was casually mentioned by Danielle some days later. The unseemly name calling by 'Him Indoors' that resulted, just goes to prove that even in a long relationship like ours, there is still room for further training and improved communication.

Non-professional paid helpers – These are often older 'Juniors' who, with a little cash incentivising, can be called upon to walk, feed or play with a dog whilst their owners are otherwise engaged. This can be a productive relationship as juniors are usually fun and don't tire easily. They also tend to be generous in the treats department and not too strict. However, some juniors are not as responsible as they should be and there can be a worrying tendency to forget their responsibilities. Teenagers, in particular, have no sense of routine, and when, on the odd occasion I was left in the care of 'Junior Him', when we were all suffering his teenage phase, I used to have some very oddly timed trips to the garden and meals, although on the up side, he had some interesting friends that he used to invite to the house when 'Them Indoors' weren't around. I think he was under the misapprehension that he'd covered his tracks, but 'Her Indoors' has been trained by me to have the eyes of a hawk, and she didn't miss a trick. The jelly under the dog basket and cigarette butts on the patio were also a bit of a clue if I'm honest.

Professional dog-walkers – These are the folk who make dog care into a business and can often be seen in sensible vans, adorned with paw-print designs and pictures of dogs, with dog crates in the back, visiting pooches in their own home. They will usually take them for lengthy walks, or can just be used for playing ball in the garden. These are best suited to permanent care arrangements, for dogs with working owners, as they tend not to be able to squeeze in clients who only need them every now and then. They have the obvious advantage of being professional dog people, fully equipped, insured, and often with qualifications that evidence a very high level of training. They can take a bit of training up in the individual needs and peccadilloes department, but if you've chosen well you can quickly bring them up to speed.

Doggy daycare – There are people who take dogs into their own homes to look after them, and this can be on a day-care basis, or for longer stays when their owners go on holiday. They usually provide a warm and friendly home environment, and I used one such arrangement for many years. This particular family had obviously been very well trained as I was allowed to sleep on their junior's bed and raided the family fridge so often they had to prop an ironing board against its door. Often these carers will have dogs of their own. This family had three Golden Retrievers who were fine, friendly dogs. There was, however, a cat!

Now I know some dogs get on fine with cats but I'm not one of those amiable creatures. My relationship with cats is restricted to sourcing their pooh in the gravel on the drive, which provides a rare delicacy for the discerning canine gourmet, something that 'Him Indoors', in spite of my best efforts over the years, has not been trained to appreciate. He, rather disappointingly, still uses one of my alternative names, usually including the words 'disgusting' and 'animal' in close proximity, when he catches me in the act of snacking; I can't think why. Suffice to say my only other relationship with cats involves chasing them down the garden and off my property. Who do they think they are?

Anyway, my holiday carers have a cat of their own and when I first saw it, I gave it the usual treatment and ran at it barking. However, this cat didn't even flinch let alone move. It just looked at me lazily and if I got too close, had a quick swipe at me with rather sharp claws. My initial reaction was complete surprise, then a grudging respect, which meant that overall, we got on fine for the duration of my stay, although it didn't affect my treatment of other felines.

The only problem with this kind of caring arrangement is when they take more than one visiting dog and you then have to put up with all kinds of canines. Sometimes they don't like you, which was the case with one particularly antisocial Patterdale Terrier who used to have a go at the other dogs at every opportunity. Then there are the dogs that I didn't like. I tend not to be generally all that good with Spaniels. It's their ears. They make them look a bit woosy plus they have a tendency to pong a bit. I don't wish to offend Spaniel-kind in general and would like to make it clear that it isn't a case of breed prejudice; there are some Spaniels that I deem to be okay. I like to keep my criteria for such preferences a closely guarded secret. It keeps 'Them Indoors' on their toes and stops them getting complacent, which is something you need to aim for with your owner. It keeps the relationship fresh.

Anyway, the net result of all of this is I now go and stay with a carer in their home, who only has one dog at a time, thus there is no chance of me being in the company of a canine I don't like or who doesn't like me. I'm also getting a bit older so I prefer a more peaceful environment where I can indulge in plenty of senior snoozing, undisturbed. Sometimes it can be a case of changing your care arrangements as your needs evolve over time. You just need to make sure that your owners are trained to be flexible and to adapt, rather than insisting on the same old arrangement, regardless.

Kennels – I'm generally of the view that kennels get an unfairly bad press. This can be because thoughtless owners tend to see them from their own point of view rather than their dog's, and consider them as a kind of canine prison. In fact, well-run kennels can offer great holiday and day care. You get your own heated and air conditioned room with secure outside space and with lots of other animals to keep you company. You can share your unmelodious vocals with the rest of the world, without complaint, and you get regular meals, treats and walks. However, it is wise to source your kennels carefully and make sure they have high standards of hygiene and care.

Personal recommendations are, as ever, the best way to find a suitable establishment. I used kennels for many years but found that as I got older, they were a bit too busy and stressful. Also, you need to beware of changes of ownership. As the business is sold as a going concern, usually the first you know about it changing hands is when you turn up and find it's different people greeting you. This is rather disconcerting as you've build a relationship of trust with the previous owner and it's not very pleasant having a change imposed on you without consultation. That aside, I would definitely recommend giving kennels a go, as I always enjoyed them when I was younger and used to trot off quite happily with the kennel maid whilst 'Her Indoors' used to look on emotionally, at my retreating rear end.

Medical Service Providers
Another, very significant care arrangement to get swiftly in place, is the one with your Vet. Choosing a Vet is again best done by recommendation. It might also be wise to compare prices for some common procedures, just to make sure that you're not spending more of your treats money than is necessary. Price should not be the over-riding consideration however, unless you own someone like 'Him Indoors' who recently suggested seeing if he could get my arthritis medication a bit cheaper on the internet. I had to put my paw down over that I can tell you. They could be selling any old dodgy drug. Whilst some of those could have pleasing side effects, I'm not taking any chances. He can just pay up and smile through gritted teeth. He knows I'm worth it.

Ideally, you need a Vet with an efficient appointment system. Ours is normally quite good and doesn't keep us waiting for very long, which is just as well because 'Her Indoors' tends to get a bit stressed. She finds my meeting and greeting of other dogs, particularly very large ones who might take exception to my no-nonsense terrier ways, a bit tense. She also gets bothered by my vocal remonstrations of non-canine animals in baskets, particularly cats, rabbits and Guinea Pigs. I don't know why she worries. Cats can look after themselves, Guinea Pigs we used to have as family pets when the Juniors were little and I studied them intensely through the wire of their grazing arch, and rabbits, well, let's put it this way, I know how to deal with them when we meet in the garden!

Once allowed through to see the Vet, you need someone who's very generous with the treats. My personal best is six biscuits in one visit, and that was just an annual check-up. 'Her Indoors', who takes personal responsibility for my waistline as well as her own, gets slightly tetchy over excessive treat giving as she reckons it's a case of double standards, but I think it's essential to smooth the passage of a consultation and compensate for any little indignities suffered. I can't think why the NHS doesn't adopt a similar policy. I bet they'd have fewer missed doctor's appointments.

Oh and by the way, it also helps if your Vet knows one or two things about animals and medicine.

So that's it, the major decisions have been made and you are about to move into your new home. Congratulations! Now you need to consider how to make the best of your new situation and start establishing some of the basic principles that underpin a happy and lasting human/dog relationship.

Chapter Two

Settling In

The early days in a new home are crucial to establishing a good relationship with your owner and family. It helps if you have some idea what to expect beforehand and to have made a few basic preparations.

Equipment
Acquiring an owner means investing in a few items of basic equipment to ensure happiness and comfort.

Outdoor clothes - Owners should already have a coat and some shoes, but it is helpful if the coat is a proper outdoor one, rather than a fashion item, as you'll have to take them out in all weathers. I am also a coat wearing pooch as I enjoy an extra layer of warmth and waterproofing, particularly as I've become more senior, but not all dogs are keen. It's entirely your decision and if your owner should be foolish enough to try and impose a coat against your better judgement, then express your displeasure clearly by refusing to co-operate with putting it on, rolling to try and get it off, or, if more subtle tactics fail, by sitting down and refusing to move. That should make the point clearly.

Owners will also need wellie boots in order for them to cope with the wet and mud, plus a nice woolly hat to make them look a complete t** when out in the winter. Gloves are useful, although they can cause problems by being dropped in the mud when juggling pooh bags and a lead, and a large umbrella, although not essential, can give hours of fun when they turn inside out in high winds, however you will need to watch your ears in the expletive department when this happens.

Leads – I recommend different leads for different occasions. I have a fixed length lead which I use getting in and out of the car, or when walking in towns and cities when I need to keep 'Her Indoors' close by me to stop her getting too distracted by shops, expensive price tags and enticing window displays.

I also have a retractable lead for when we are out in the countryside. These have the advantage of providing extra exercise for your family. I always ensure that when I'm on a long lead, I change my mind constantly about which side of the road I want to walk on. This is particularly effective when walking with more than one person as they have to keep swapping sides, like slow motion country dancing, in order to avoid tangling the other person in the lead. It works best however if you walk with another dog who's also got their owner on an extendable lead. Then you can both swap sides constantly, wrapping the leads around each other until it looks like one of 'Junior Her's' less successful attempts at knitting. However, it does greatly increase your owner's manual dexterity.

When I was younger, I used to let 'Her Indoors' off the leash so that I could dash around exploring and sniffing at my own pace. However, as I've got older I've gone a bit deaf so, after years of faking selective hearing, I now genuinely cannot hear her calling me back and I get a bit worried that she'll go off without me and we'll lose each other. This actually happened to my friend, Charlie, an aging Sussex Spaniel. He is normally walked with a much younger dog, the only other Border Terrier in the village, but because she is so speedy, he lingers way behind and his owner does a whole circuit of the playing field without him, picking him up on the way out. This arrangement led to a genuine misunderstanding when a well-meaning lady pulled up in the village hall car park and saw Charlie on his own. Fearing he'd been lost, and with no owner in sight, she was worried he'd wander out onto the road, so she picked him up and took him home with her.

When Charlie's owner came back, Charlie had gone, resulting in an extensive search of the surrounding gardens and countryside, involving half the village. Anyway, all ended well as the lady who found Charlie, posted a photo of him on Facebook and all were happily re-united. Still, it goes to prove that you can't just let your owner wander off any old how, you need to keep them safe and close by.

Cars – Although we dogs are usually capable of walking for miles, there are times when it will be necessary for you to travel further distances and this is when a car comes in handy. Now I have a fascination with car interiors and regularly have to be pulled out of the foot-well of complete strangers' cars. I also like trades vans as there are usually all sorts of things hidden in the back for the enquiring dog to discover.

'Him Indoors' owns a Honda CRV which is nice and roomy and comfy. He is, however, a bit precious about the interior so I choose to travel in a soft crate with mesh sides so that I can still keep an eye on what's going on and comment on the driving, other road users, the view or anything else that takes my fancy for that matter. I also like to give an early warning when we arriving at our destination with a distinctive yowling noise which is quite impressive in the close confinement of a car. Unfortunately, 'Them Indoors' fail to appreciate my little contribution, especially when I get it wrong and start up when we've slowed down for traffic queues, junctions or roundabouts.

'Her Indoors' has what can only be described as a mid-life crisis car: a Mini convertible. She reckons she's saved from it being a cry for help by the fact that it isn't red with go-faster stripes, but I think she's deluded. It's a final fling before settling down with a comfortable silver hatchback that is so economical the government pays you to drive it. There is no room in the boot of a Mini convertible for a dog, even a small one like me, and my

25

soft travel crate won't fit on the bucket seats, so she's bought me one of those dog car seats that are suspended slightly above the base of the seat, by a strap around the headrest. This has the advantage of giving you a good view of the road, although this can be a mixed blessing with 'Her Indoors' driving technique. However, it is good on sunny days when we have the roof down. I don't know about other dogs but I love the wind streaming through my ears and being able to sniff the air. It also gives me direct access to express my views to other road users, something 'Her Indoors' takes exception to. I don't know why, she does it, and her language is far worse than mine.

'Junior Him' used to have his own car when he lived at home. It was actually an old Toyota Yaris that used to belong to 'Her Indoors' in her sensible days, and he hardly ever cleaned it which made it quite exciting. You never knew what you'd find in the detritus but it was occasionally edible, even if a bit fluffy. I don't think I ever went in it with 'Junior Him' driving which is probably just as well. I don't like sudden breaking. 'Junior Her' started learning to drive but she had a little upset with the driving instructor. 'Junior Her' is an intelligent person but she's never quite mastered her 'left' and 'right'. When she was a young girl, and used to enter karate competitions, 'Her Indoors' used to write an 'L' and an 'R' on the appropriate hands to aid her in her judgments. Perhaps this is something they should have carried over to driving lessons as on one occasion 'Junior Her' tried to turn right, when she'd actually been asked to turn left, leading to a virtual nervous breakdown on behalf of her Instructor and 'Junior Her' coming home in tears. I would personally have liked to give him a bite on the bum for such behaviour. Even if his life was in danger, that's no excuse for making a young woman cry. He's clearly not a dog-owner that's for sure. No self-respecting pooch would allow such a carry-on.

Beds – All people should have their own beds and you should make a decision about where, in relation to theirs, you want yours to be situated. Some dogs go in the bedroom, but in our household, the snoring, hair, emissions and bad breath are not tolerated and I choose to sleep in the kitchen away from such unpleasantness.

I spend a lot of time in this room as it's the best in the house. It's where people tend to congregate and where all the food is prepared. My bed is next to the back door which leads into the lobby where all my food and equipment are kept. This is an ideal location. I can keep an eye on the comings and goings, greeting people appropriately. I used to leap out of bed with delirious joy when I was younger, but now I save getting out of bed for visitors, who have clearly only come to see me. With the family, I just roll over and expose my tummy for some passing tickling, a pleasurable greeting that involves minimal effort for a dog of my senior years.

Personal space - Now sociable creatures that we are, we dogs sometimes need some quiet time and personal space and you will need to be insistent on this from the outset. It can be achieved by the use of an indoor dog crate, suitably furnished with cushions, toys and blankets, where a pooch can shut themselves away. Some dogs go even further and have their own accommodation in a kennel in the garden, but I personally think that is taking things a bit too far. I like to keep an eye on my family and check what they're up to, so my answer to the personal space issue is to have a stair-gate on the kitchen door so that access is controlled. Occasionally it is accidentally left open during the day and then I have a little wander. I always aim to get in 'Him Indoors' study as this is a bit of a man cave, with interesting stuff at small dog height. He usually tries to remember to shut the door but he sometimes forgets. I like to have a root around in the waste paper basket, emptying the contents on the floor and shredding up small pieces of paper. This tends to upset 'Them Indoors'- I can't think why. After all, there's an electric machine in the corner of the study that they paid good money for and which only serves the same purpose. I'd have obliged if they'd only thought to ask nicely.

I do allow my family to socialise with me in the rest of the house of an evening, particularly in the lounge. 'Her Indoors' made a bean bag with some off-cuts of soft-furnishing fabric, and I have requisitioned it for my personal use. It took a bit of getting used to and some unsympathetic mirth from 'Her Indoors' when my bottom end slid downhill after I'd been wriggling a bit too much, but I've mastered the technique now. It does provide a very supportive sleeping surface for a dog, and I like mine positioned in front of the woodburner in the winter so I can toast my paws and watch the TV at the same time. Bliss.

The First Twenty-four Hours

The journey home – You will, of course, have your travel arrangements in place, but it is important to allow your owner and family to start adjusting to travelling with a canine, particularly if they're first time owners. If they go too fast around the corners or don't stop frequently enough, especially if you're a pup with limited capacity in the 'holding-on' department, then you must vomit, wee or pooh, ideally all three, in the car. I know this seems like tough treatment, but the sooner your family have mastered the basics of car transportation, the better. It is possible that they might get a bit stressed on this first journey, so make sure you use your appealing eyes and a bit of shaking if necessary, to smooth any unpleasantness.

On arrival – Once you get to your home, unless the weather is particularly inclement or it's dark, I suggest you immediately check out your outside environment as this is going to be very important to you in the weeks and months ahead. I know you might be desperate to go to the loo after a car journey, but try to hang on if you can. Sniff all the shrubs and trees in an interested way but refuse to oblige, particularly if they indulge in strange rituals such as telling you to 'be busy'. What's that all about? Instead, wait until you're inside the comfort of your new home, preferably on the carpet, then have a good wee and pooh in the warm. It'll start them getting used to the idea that one of their significant roles as an owner is to clear up after you.

You need to start getting your owners into a routine straight away. It helps if they know when to feed you, take you outside in the garden, and walk you, if appropriate, in those early days. It is up to you to guide this. Hopefully, they'll have already had some advice from the breeder or re-homing centre so make sure they conform with that. Just use your expressions, particularly your eyes, and your body language, plus a bit of whimpering, to make your expectations clear.

The first night can be a bit tricky. It might be that your owners can get through it without the need to check on you, but if they interrupt your nightly activities, especially if you are contentedly sleeping, make sure you get some benefit and make them play with you, preferably with a toy that squeaks. If they don't check on you, and you feel that it is appropriate for them to do so, don't hesitate to interrupt their sleep. Remember to look all lost and forlorn when they come to you, then when they have comforted you, introduce the game so that you can get the full benefit. If necessary, repeat this action several times during the night and they'll soon get the hang of things. Don't worry, if you're a bit tired in the morning you can always have a lie-in whilst they busy themselves with the chores. Then, just as they're flagging, you can wake up bright-eyed and bushy tailed, ready for mischief and fun.

Visitors – Try and dissuade visitors for the first twenty-four hours at least. You'll need time to get your humans to settle and for you to check your environment and ensure that you've got everything they need. After that, particularly if you are a puppy, it'll be almost impossible to stop them, so give in with good grace and make sure that they bring you a toy as a welcome present.

The Pack Hierarchy

One of the important things to establish from the outset is the pack hierarchy and to make sure that your owner and family understand your place within it. There will already be an order, so you first need to grasp what that is. You may have got some clues from when you had them visit in the first instance.

Male-dominated – This is quite an old-fashioned set up and can be easily confused with one of the other categories, so make sure you've got this right. The adult male, whether they are your owner or not, will have the final say over all major decisions. They can be quite difficult to train as they are used to being the centre of attention and are not used to having any significant challenges to their authority. You'll need to move quickly to establish that such behaviour is firmly in the past. You are in charge now and they better get used to it.

Appears male-dominated but isn't – This is a common situation, particularly with middle-aged humans. They were brought up in an era when men dominated households, so might superficially cling to some of the behaviours of the male-dominated set-up, but actually it is the woman who holds the lead. In order for harmony to be maintained, there is a pretence that she doesn't, but nobody is fooled, least of all you. It can sometimes be a good idea to play along, but generally, just get in there and let them know who's boss.

Female dominated- This is an increasingly common situation, particularly amongst younger women who know their place in the world and what women are capable of. They don't take any nonsense but are usually soft-hearted which is what allows you the opportunity to make it clear that when the dog biscuits are down, you're in charge.

Single gender households – Again, this is increasingly common, but the same basic rules apply. One person is usually dominant, it's just a question of digging behind appearances and working out which one it is. You then need to gently but firmly put them in their place: behind you.

Equal households – This is an ideal that lots aspire to, and many think they have achieved, but in reality is usually one of the above situations. If there is a genuine equality of power, then there won't be for much longer. You will be in charge moving forward.

Health Checks
Within the first week or so, you will need to establish the health needs of your family. You won't be allowed to accompany them to their doctor's unless you are an assistance dog, although they will accompany you to yours which is a bit unfair. However, as doctors don't do biscuits and often run behind with their appointments, to be frank, you're not missing much.

It might be that your family have specific health needs that you will want to help with. Sometimes owners are in wheelchairs, have sight or hearing impairments, or maybe mental health issues. They will need additional training if they are to get the full benefit of your attentions, but it can be very rewarding to own people who really need you. Sometimes the caring role is a more informal one. Elderly, single owners might need to keep you company, and children with conditions such as autism, can be taught many life skills by an obliging canine friend.

Make sure that you don't neglect your own health and that you get to meet your Vet in those early days. As well as directly assisting with your requirements, they can also be helpful sources of advice in the training of people. Many problems are quite common and the solutions can be simple, so don't struggle on, re-inventing the wheel, seek assistance.

Diet
This is rather a delicate issue, since many humans are overweight, some of them seriously so, and it can be a very difficult one to address. You must make sure that you get them out for plenty of exercise which will help shift a few pounds. You can also try and get them to appreciate healthy eating by showing them the right kind of snacking to indulge in. I've yet to meet a pooch that doesn't like carrot and apples, so make this very clear to your humans and hopefully they'll follow your lead, if you'll excuse the pun.

Whatever you do, don't be tempted to try and solve the problem by eating the excess yourself, otherwise you'll end up fat too. There's no sorrier sight than an overweight dog leading an overweight owner as they both waddle up the road. A good example of dogs who had avoided this trap came with two Basset Hounds being walked locally by a rather large middle aged man who was huffing and puffing up a hill accompanied by his two very trim dogs. We stopped to have a little chat and 'Her Indoors' admired the dogs who were in fine fettle. The man, after getting his breath back and having a little rest, told 'Her Indoors' all about the tendency for Basset Hounds to be overfed and overweight, which is a particular hazard when your tummy is already that close to the floor. He then gave an admirable lecture on diet and exercise, and departed, slowly manoeuvring his bulk along, wheezing asthmatically, up the hill. Now I'm not a dog to pass judgement, but I think the principles of good diet apply to people as much as to dogs.

There are some foods that you can happily take off your humans without risking any harm to yourself. Chicken and cheese have got to be up there, at the top of my list. I also have a real weakness for beef stew, made even more delicious by the pleasure of anticipation as it takes a long time to cook, and then an age to cool down so that I can get my just rewards. However, there are some food that you can let your humans eat which you mustn't touch yourself, like chocolate. Humans love the stuff, and women in particular will do almost anything to get it. I know 'Her Indoors' gets very grumpy indeed if there is none in the house, although at her age she needs to watch it. A second on the lips, a life time on the hips. Anyway, chocolate is poisonous to dogs so don't be tempted to try it. A friend of mine, a Gordon Setter called Indie, made the mistake of eating half a chocolate gateaux, which her otherwise well-trained family had accidentally left out. She had to go to the Vet's and have an injection to make her bring it all up again. Apart from anything else that's a terrible waste of cake.

There is lots of good advice out there on the appropriate diet for humans although sometimes it is rather contradictory. Here are just a few examples:

- A modest consumption of red wine is good for them. It helps prevent respiratory disease, contains antioxidants, stops them getting colds and can help prevent Herpes and Alzheimer's / All alcohol is poison, increases their chance of getting cancer and they shouldn't touch a drop unless they have a premature death wish.

- A few squares of chocolate are good for them and can help their heart, circulation and brain / Sugar is the new opiate of the masses, rots their teeth and overloads the liver. It should be taxed to the hilt to prevent consumption by people who just don't know what's good for them.

- Fruit juice contains vitamin C and counts as one of their five-a-day / Fruit juice is as bad for them as Coca Cola and has been banned in some primary schools.

- People who eat lean red meat get more protein, zinc, potassium and B vitamins than people that don't /Eating red meat significantly increases their chances of heart disease and cancer. If they regularly eat processed meat they'd better make their will immediately, they won't last long.

My personal view, for what it's worth, is that following 'Her Indoors' old Nan's advice seems a reasonable idea. She used to hold the view that 'a little bit of what you fancy does you good' tempered by 'moderation in all things'. She lived to a ripe old age so this is the mantra I think all people should follow. As for us dogs, I don't worry too much. It's all grist to my mill as far as I'm concerned and if I get it wrong and eat something that really isn't edible, it usually finds its own way out, from one end or the other, and 'Her Indoors' has been well trained in the clearing up department.

Exercise

Another essential ingredient in keeping your humans fit and well is to take them for regular exercise. Now most people, unless they suffer from any medical conditions or are elderly and frail, will quite frankly benefit from as much exercise as you are prepared to give them. However, you do need to consider you own well-being. Some dog breeds are capable of walking for miles, but for some, such as the giant breeds, too much exercise can be harmful. You also need to be careful if you are a pup, and build up your exercise gently, so you don't put too much of a strain on your growing muscles and joints. I still suffer from an unfortunate incident in my youth when I strained something hurdling the Guinea Pig grazing arch, Grand National style, and had to be taken, out of hours to the Vet. 'Him Indoors' did lots of moaning about the cost, but, more importantly, I now have arthritis in that shoulder, which slows me up a bit. However, the tablets I take are very good, and as the Vet rightly said, I'm just paying the price for fourteen years of mega-zooming.

Some dogs are so keen that they take their humans out running or cycling. This can be a mutually beneficial activity, subject to the above caveats, but whatever you do, don't allow them to dress you in Lycra and try and dissuade them from doing so too. It's harmful to the well-being of the general population who might see them and it damages your street credibility. If they acquire some, I suggest some tactical chewing where possible. That should sort it.

There are some good ways to involve your humans in such activities without risking over exerting yourself. As I've got older, I've also had to be a bit more innovative about supervising 'Him and Her Indoors' when out on very long walks. I've got them a doggy back pack that I sit in whilst they carry me. Not only does this give me a great view of the surrounding countryside but it also increases the exercise for whichever one is carrying me, which has got to be good. I might only be a small dog but after a few miles I can feel quite heavy. If you're a larger breed, this really isn't going to work for you, but I'm sure you can come up with your own solutions. We dogs are very innovative.

Chapter Three

House Rules

By now, your family should be beginning to get the idea of what being owned by a dog is all about. After this initial good start, your need to ensure you reinforce the principles by some consistency in the arrangements around home.

Personal Property
It's probable that your family, particularly if they've not been owned by a dog before, will think that everything in the house belongs to them. Nothing could be further from the truth and you need to establish the rules as soon as possible.

The dog rules of ownership
    1. If you want it, it's yours
    2. If they want it, it's yours

3. If you wanted it, then lost interest, but want it again now, it's yours
4. If you find it, it's yours
5. If they've thrown it in the bin, it's yours
6. If you can reach it, however high up it's been placed, it's yours
7. If they drop it, it's yours
8. If it's new, cherished, and/or expensive it's definitely yours
9. If it's the last sausage on the barbeque, by divine right, it's yours
10. If you're sick, miserable, bored, curious, or just downright mischievous and it would alleviate your suffering, it's yours.

Sometimes people can get a bit possessive about items of furniture. Whilst you might have a lovely dog bed, cosily lined with fleecy cushions and filled with more toys than Hamleys, it is important that you make an effort to quash this kind of behaviour from the outset.

Sofas – You can allow people to sit on the sofa but you must ensure that you take up as much space as possible so that they are uncomfortably squashed up in the corner. This is easy to do if you are a big dog, but takes a bit more practice if you are small. You need to adopt a sleeping position with your legs extended as far as they can go, and ideally, with your hind legs splayed width-wise. Whilst this can look a bit undignified, don't worry, it's actually quite comfortable. If you need a bit of extra padding or warmth, try lying directly on them. They make good pillows or cushions.

Beds – As I've already mentioned, it's entirely your decision as to whether or not you share their bed or sleep in your own. If you decide to supervise them over-night, the same rules about maximising the space you take up apply as they do to sofa napping. If they indulge in any unacceptable behaviours or emissions of any sort during the night, feel free to disturb their sleep. If they are a bit tardy in the getting up department, particularly at the weekend, a good tip is to feign retching. That'll get them out like a shot!

If you decide to sleep on their bed during the day, when they are not in it, don't worry about any dirty paws or wet fur and if you've rolled in something delightful, like fox pooh, so much the better, that's what bedding is for.

Rugs – Sometimes people can labour under the misapprehension that rugs are purely decorative; you need to quickly disabuse them of this fact. Rugs are there to provide dogs with convenient staging posts for little naps, all around the house. If the rug is coarsely textured, they are really good for back scratching, wiping drool, or in the case of senior dogs, removing eye bogies. If they are soft then they can still be used for wiping muddy paws or a wet coat, but they are best as a comfortable insulating layer between a dog and the floor for those little sleeps that a dog needs to get him or her through the day. Cushions can serve a similar purpose and the more expensive and luxurious they are the better. You know you're worth it.

Net curtains – Again people can be under the misapprehension that net curtains are there to provide them with a degree of privacy from their neighbours. This is slightly misplaced and you need to get them to understand that they are actually there, like most things in the house, for you. You can watch what's going on through the little holes, whether that's visitors approaching, neighbouring cats, other dogs walking by, birds visiting the garden, or even better squirrels. You can lull them into a false sense of security, then poke your head under the net curtain and let rip. It offers the additional pleasure of surprise.

Hot and Cold Spots
Now people usually have an instinctive understanding of the need to keep warm or cool off, as appropriate, and basking in the sunshine is something that people crave as much as animals, it's just that we dogs are better at it. People usually indulge in expensive holidays to lie on sun-loungers soaking up the rays, but we dogs can do this in our own homes, even in the most unpromising of climates, so it's up to you to lead the way by example.

I know all the best spots for sun puddling, both inside and out, and it is important that you train your family to facilitate or even help with this process. In my room, the kitchen, there is a window that lets the sun shine directly in during the afternoon, when the sun is on the back of the house. In the morning however, the sun shines on the front windows, including a window half way up the stair case. If the kitchen door is kept open, this provides a pleasing patch of sunlight in the middle of the kitchen floor that moves around a bit as the morning progresses. Once I'd mastered getting the family to oblige in the door department, the next stage was to get them to show awareness that I might be lying directly in the way and that this position might subtly change. I certainly didn't want to have to disturb myself and move every time they needed a cup of tea, so instead I've trained them to keep their eyes open and carefully step over me.

The same applies in the garden. Once I have finished getting 'Him and Her Indoors' to play ball and have tired of supervising them in their various activities, I've trained them to leave me alone for a spot of outdoor sun-puddling. I know all the best spots. Next to the back door, leaning against the brick wall which acts as a kind of radiator when the sun is on it, is rather pleasant. The end wall of 'Her Indoors' garden office is also very good. It's painted matt black which is the best colour for absorbing the sun's rays, and is also sheltered from the prevailing wind, so I can often be found snoozing there. It has the added advantage of affording me a good view of the garden so I can ensure that 'Them Indoors' are not slacking.

The need for heating appliances is often something that is misunderstood. People sometimes seem to labour under the misapprehension that they are provided for them. What nonsense! You clearly don't want your family getting all over-heated so you should have no compunction about placing yourself between a person and a source of heat, getting first shot at absorbing the rays. In the winter we have the luxury of a wood burner. Now as I'm only a small dog it just isn't possible to absorb all the heat, but I give it my best shot. I lie as close to it as I can possibly manage, panting heavily. I sometimes need to nip into the kitchen for a little drink of water to cool myself down, but it's a sacrifice I'm willing to make to prevent 'Them Indoors' from over-heating. If they don't have the wood burner lit, they have a little fan heater, and I sit so close that I'm almost touching it. The same principle can be applied to radiators. You don't want your family to risk getting too close, but you can lean against them and toast your nether regions. I've seen photos of pooches applying themselves to similarly protecting their family from Range-style cookers. The principle is the same, so just use your initiative

The same theories are applied to keeping cool, although in the United Kingdom, this is something that we only have to worry about for a few weeks every year, but that increases if you are a pooch with a heavy coat. Dogs with short coats can often fend for themselves, seeking out cool ceramic tiled floors indoors, and cold paving slabs outside. Occasionally, if it's very warm, I join 'Her Indoors' in her office in the garden. She has a revolving electric fan and I make sure that I lie in a good position so that I can feel its benefit. Sometimes, if I pant hard and look particularly uncomfortable, 'Her Indoors' fixes the fan so it points in one direction: at me. I can then enjoy the full benefit. 'Her Indoors' gets a bit hot but she just has to put up with it. After all, I'm the one with the fur.

A couple of my friends on Twitter are Briards. This is a large breed of dog with a thick heavy coat. They've had to give their humans special training so that they provide their canine companions with their very own paddling pool in the hot weather. They can wander in and out at will, keeping themselves nice and cool and, with the occasional good shake, sharing that benefit with their families too.

There are also some dogs who've trained their humans to buy special cooling pads, a bit like a large ice-pack, for dogs to lie on and you can also buy dog ice-creams. I don't trouble myself with those, I just have fun trying to get my fair share of the families, after all, they seem incapable of eating an ice-cream or lolly without dropping some of it on the floor and I'm very happy to oblige in the cleaning up department.

Visitors

It is important that you ensure your family are well socialised and this means encouraging visitors to the house. Some dogs can get a bit defensive of their humans, but with the obvious caveat of ensuring that visitors are suitable people to be calling at your home, it is best to be welcoming so that your family can benefit from some healthy interaction.

Your humans might well labour under the common apprehension that people call to see them, whereas as all dogs know, every visitor to the house has come to see us. You need to get in there quickly, as soon as they walk through the door, and offer an appropriate greeting. Some dogs like to jump up which is fine if you're a small dog, but if you are larger you need to be careful. You don't want to be responsible for knocking anyone over or they might not call again. Some people can also be surprisingly unforgiving about paw marks, claw scratches and dog hair, but that sort of fastidiousness is not to be tolerated. A little bit of dirt never did anyone any harm and what do they think clothes brushes are for?

One thing to be aware of with visitors is that they often don't know what the house rules are. This can be a disadvantage as they can lead your owner astray with drinks, unhealthy treats, bunches of flowers (what is that all about for goodness sake?) and chat of the sort that doesn't involve you in your rightful place at the centre of the universe. It's up to you how much of this you tolerate, but if it gets too much I'd advise suitable distraction techniques such as removing drinks and snacks when they are not paying attention and lying on your back and kicking your legs in the air to attract notice. That usually sorts it.

When 'Her Indoors' was growing up, they had a Labrador/Rough Collie cross as a family pet. One evening, 'Her Indoors' parents were going out so the neighbour came round to baby sit and the dog clearly felt that he wasn't getting enough of the attention so he did his party piece. This involved lying on his back with his tongue lolling out and his eyes rolled back a bit so he could keep an eye on his subject and gauge their reaction. He would then thrust his legs skyward, with a vocal accompaniment, in a kind of spasmodic, jerky movement. As he was quite a large dog this was an impressive sight. Unfortunately, the lady in question hadn't ever had a dog of her own and was completely untrained. She thought he was having some kind of fit and was thrown into panic about what to do next. Fortunately, realising his audience was not responding in the approved manner, he stopped, so he was saved a trip to the emergency Vets, but it just goes to show how careful you need to be with visitors to your house.

Delivery Drivers, Postal Workers, Refuse Collectors and Unsolicited Callers to the House

Most people have an amiable trusting instinct when it comes to others of their kind, and they seem to believe that people delivering or calling at the house, are okay. We dogs know otherwise and it is our duty to make sure our families are fully informed and, if necessary, protected from themselves. They might think that the box contains a new printer, the parcel a book from Amazon, or the bag yet another new piece of clothing for 'Her Indoors' or 'Junior Her' but what they don't know is they have potential to contain unknown terrors that only a canine can detect. And those that deliver them are clearly part of this alien subterfuge. It is left to us dogs to let them know, in no uncertain terms, that we are on to them.

This can occasionally be misunderstood. I once sneaked out of the gate and gave our postman a thorough telling off for having the audacity to deliver a package without my explicit approval. This lead to a stiff letter from the Post Office saying that if I did it again, they would stop delivering post to our house. 'Her Indoors' was rightly mortified, as she is ultimately responsible for securing the boundaries, but I'd like to point out, in my defence, that no harm was actually done, I just sounded stern which is, apparently, enough. Anyway, the Postman we have now is a much more enlightened chap who understands the distress caused to us dogs, and brings a biscuit in recompense. Even if he doesn't see me, he leaves a treat for me in the parcel box, but this is a very high level of training that most pooches can't quite manage.

The other visitors to the house that people tolerate and which dogs generally find unacceptable, are the refuse collectors. Whilst taking the rubbish away is clearly a necessary function, the presence of a big, noisy, polluting lorry and all the banging and shouting that emptying the bins seems to necessitate, is a cue for you to express your displeasure at the whole process. In these days of recycling, when waste is often divided up into three separate collections, you need to be vigilante to ensure that you don't miss a collection. With a bit of luck they will drop something smelly that was once vaguely edible which you can investigate and consume should you wish to do so.

With anyone else that comes to the house, you are duty bound to check their suitability and you should train your family to take notice of your views. I was the deciding factor in which company 'Them Indoors' chose to replace their windows. One man came round who smelt very strongly of cigarette smoke which offended my delicate sense of smell. He also tried too hard to ingratiate himself by disturbing me whilst I was sleeping, poking his face right up to mine. He's lucky I didn't bite him on the nose but I did bark rather sharply and make him jump. As I'm normally friendly to strangers, 'Them Indoors' took my judgement very seriously and placed an order with a different company whose representative knew how to correctly greet a dog. As it turned out, by placing an order they were automatically entered into a competition which they ended up wining and got themselves an all-expenses paid trip to Paris. I notice I wasn't included which was a bit ungrateful as it was me that secured the company the order in the first place. Still, I did have a very nice weekend with 'Junior Him and Her' at the grandparents, so I didn't come out of it too badly.

The Family Routine

Some dogs are quite lax in their attitude towards routine, but I always think it's best to establish a regular timetable with your family, reinforced with gentle reminders where necessary, so that everyone knows where they stand. And it's not just the timing of events, it's also about targeting your training at different family members so that they are all involved in your care.

The time at which you allow your family to get up and go to sleep is largely a matter of personal preference. You might want to consider different times for weekdays, when your family will probably have work and school, and weekends when you should allow them to relax a little and recharge their batteries so that they can spend some quality time with you. Don't be influenced in your own wake-up time by that of your families. With my domestic set-up, I allow 'Him Indoors' to get himself ready, have his breakfast and unload the dishwasher. I then demand my breakfast and, after I've eaten it, I have another little nap until 'Her Indoors' appears. As I'm a senior dog, I expect 'Her Indoors' to come to my basket to greet me, and restrict my actions to rolling over so she can tickle my tummy in just the right spot. Unless I'm needed to clear up any dropped food, I stay in bed until the exact moment, just after she's cleaned her teeth, when I know she will put her coat on for our walk. I wait by the kitchen door and if she deviates from the agreed routine in any way, however small, I reprimand her with dirty looks, or barking. I know this might seem strict but the morning walk is a very important part of the day.

Similarly, I'm very strict about my dinner time: 5.00pm on the dot, and about the evening trip to the garden before bed. This doesn't mean however, that you cannot vary the routine if you wish to. Should you feel like getting up early, then bark and wake them up. Equally, if you don't fancy taking them out in the garden last thing at night, charge for your compliance with a treat.

However, if they try and vary the arrangements you need to take a very dim view. Even if they've got a reasonable excuse, like the clocks going backwards or forwards at different times of the year, make them suffer for the inconvenience and distress caused. Whilst they might not be personally responsible, it wasn't us dogs who decided to interfere with the natural order of things just to buy some extra daylight hours at a convenient time of day.

I'm also a firm believer in training juniors properly. I had 'Junior Her' out in the garden every day after school playing ball with me and she was also given the honour of serving my tea. 'Junior Him' was very good in the football department although he had to be reminded that the point of a football is to let your dog catch it and carry it round, puncturing it if necessary. He seemed to have some strange, alternative ideas from watching football on the television but I soon put him right.

It's best to select one person to train in the more intimate duties of dog care. In my case, it's always been 'Her Indoors'. She's quite practical and careful so I trust her with grooming me and any minor medical needs such as administering drugs or treating injuries. The fact that she's brought up two children means she's not too squeamish in the area of bodily excretions, and she's the one that usually gets the job of picking up my little offerings. Should she not make a thorough job of this, I start to clear up myself, which usually results in me being called by one of my alternative names involving the word 'disgusting'. Still, she's only got herself to blame, she should be a bit quicker off the mark.

You might need to make some adjustments to your family routine depending on the season. For example, in the summer, 'Her Indoors' and I have an evening garden patrol after we've had our tea and we both value this time spent together. I allow her to water the plants, something I regularly help with myself, and we wander around inspecting them, with her keeping up a little running commentary about the health, growth and performance of the various individuals that she lovingly tends. It's always a nice time of day and it is something that we are reluctant to let go of, come the autumn, when the nights start drawing in.

With 'Him Indoors', I accompany him on the serious business of pest control. We've got a reasonable size country garden so we are plagued with all kinds of undesirables: rabbits, moles, mice rats, rats with tails called grey squirrels, and pigeons to name just a few. I've managed to catch most things but the moles and the squirrels have evaded me, so far. Moles have a sneaky habit of disappearing underground in little tunnels too small for even the most optimistic terrier to venture into, and squirrels use a similarly dirty tactic and take to the tree tops. I have flung myself a fair height up a tree trunk in pursuit of a squirrel, but I can't climb to the very top. I'm a dog not a cat. 'Her Indoors' was once walking along under some trees, when a squirrel missed its footing and dropped out of a tree and onto the ground directly in front of her. I've spent a whole life-time waiting for that to happen to me, but so far without luck.

The important thing with domestic duties is to only do the ones that you want to, and get your family to do the others. Some dogs don't like chasing vermin so if that's the case, don't do it and let your family find their own solution to the problem. Although it may not always seem like it, people are generally quite intelligent, so it's a good idea to let them exercise their brain power on some harmless problems, rather than rushing to help them out every few minutes. If you have a particular interest, like sniffing things out, then train a member of your family to take an amiable interest in a suitable activity, such as drag hunting, so that you can freely indulge your canine nature. After all, mutual benefit is the name of the game so if you want to do something, get your family to help.

Chapter Four

Basic Training

Now that you've established the fundamental principles and routine of everyday life with your family, the next step is to work on some basic training. We've all seen examples, when we've been out walking, of people who haven't been trained by their pooches, and, to be honest, it's not a pretty sight. Shocking though it is to consider, there are people left roaming free, not on the lead or under direct control, worrying other animals and people with their unrestrained behaviour. There are also people who ignore basic commands and don't pick up after their dogs risking a brush with the enforcers of local bye laws as well as just being plain anti-sociable. If you have taken on a family, remember that it is your responsibility to put effort in during those early days.

Walking on a Lead

There are some dogs and their humans who can manage without a lead and never stray far from each other, but this is not something I personally recommend. However certain you think you are, an unforeseen event can lead to disaster, and off-lead is something that, in most canine/human relationships, should be reserved for those who can manage basic recall and are in a suitably unconfined environment.

Equipment

Leads, collars and harnesses – Quite clearly, you are going to need a lead to attach yourself to your walking companion, and it is up to you to decide what kind of lead you would like. As previously mentioned, fixed length leads are ideal for busy places with lots of hazards and distractions, whilst retractable leads can be good for more informal environments.

As we dogs don't have hands, you will need to provide a convenient attachment point. When I was younger, I used a collar, but being a small dog, exerting the necessary pulling power needed to direct the lead-bearer in the right direction and at the correct speed, put an undue strain on my neck so we quickly reverted to a harness. You need to take the time to find a comfortable one that fits properly or can be adjusted until it does. You also need to ensure that they are a suitable colour. I have known a few male Border Terriers who have sported pink, or as we call it, terrier orange, harnesses, and they can carry off that look as only a dog secure in his masculinity can. Guarding breeds like Rottweilers and

Dobermans can also wear pink without risk. Even if they look like a big girl's blouse, no-one is going to say anything anyway. Whatever happens, don't let your human impose any old colour on you. Make sure you get a choice. I like to wear red as it goes with my red grizzle colouring and it also has a pleasing association with danger.

If you walk your human in the dark, which is often unavoidable at certain times of year, it might be worth investing in a fluorescent or illuminated collar or harness. True, you can get your human to wear or carry something suitable of their own, but I find when it comes to safety that you can't be too careful and that it's a good idea to take things under your own control. We did however have an unforeseen difficulty when I started wearing an illuminated collar one year, around Christmas time, as I was also wearing a seasonally appropriate red coat with a white fur trim. The addition of illumination made me look so much like an animated Christmas decoration that drivers were slowing down to have a look. 'Her Indoors' was fearful of causing an accident, so we felt we had no option but to forgo the illuminated collar in the interests of the safety of other road users.

Pooh bags – You need to make sure that your humans are equipped with a suitable receptacle for picking up your poop and disposing of it in a nearby bin. I've seen all kinds of things used: nappy sacks, carrier bags and tissues to name just a few. I personally favour the kind of bags that come in a roll for tearing off, that way your lead-bearer is unlikely to run out. The only disadvantage with having them in a roll is that the serrations sometimes don't work and the bag gets ripped. This is okay if noticed and accounted for, but if not it usually results in bad language and tissues being deployed. Also, when the individual bags are separated from the roll, the sides usually stick together. The best way of getting them to separate is with wet fingers, best achieved by your human licking them, but, bearing in mind the nature of the task, licking can seem a bit unhygienic. Don't allow your human to buy cheap bags as this is always a false economy. They are often too thin and prone to splitting. They can also be rather small which is fine if you are a toy breed but rather unfortunate if you are a Great Dane. Some rolls of bags come in containers that get attached to the dog but I'm not in favour of this. After all, what do you have staff for.

In order to train your human in the correct technique for picking up after you, you need to ensure they get plenty of practice. You therefore need to perfect the art of poohing in instalments. Pooh once and wait for them to pick it up with a bag and knot the top, then move on a few steps and repeat the performance so that they have to deploy a second bag. With practice, you might even be able to extend this to a third repeat which will ensure they've fully mastered the art. A development of this technique can be used when a pooh bin is relatively close at hand. In this instance, allow them to pick up, take the used bag to the bin and return, before walking a short distance and moving onto the second step. Again, repeat for a third time if you can manage it. This scenario has the additional advantage of providing extra exercise.

Sometimes there isn't a bin close at hand which provides a particular dilemma. For some reason 'Her

Indoors' was never very keen on putting the used bag in her pocket which would have offered a sensible solution. She also doesn't like carrying it around with her as it gives her a bit of a problem when she sees someone she knows at a distance who waves at her. Does she wave back with the lead hand and risk suspending me in mid-air, or does she wave back with a pooh bag dangling? She's never really found an acceptable compromise so normally relies on just smiling and hoping they're close enough to see it. Sometimes, if a bin isn't nearby, people leave the pooh bag hanging on a bush or tree with the intention of picking it up on the way back. This clearly only works if you intend to come back along the same route and even then you run the risk of your human forgetting it and leaving it hanging there like a rather unusual Christmas Tree decoration.

You need to beware of your family deploying your pooh bags for alternative purposes, especially since the five pence levy on carrier bags has been introduced. It has been known for 'Her Indoors' to use them in extremis, as a rain hat. She also regularly uses them in the late summer and early autumn for blackberry picking. As she always has some with her and they are leak proof she finds them ideal for the purpose. When she has taken them home and emptied the bag of its blackberries, she then rinses them out and keeps them for the intended purpose, which I must admit is admirably frugal. However, I think she's taking a bit of a risk. As a quantity of blackberries look not unlike the intended contents for the bags, it's surely only a matter of time before she gets confused and throws the wrong bag away. All I know is that when this happens, it is bound, in some obscure way that is impossible to fathom, to be my fault.

Having established the correct equipment, the next step is to train your lead-bearer in the correct way to walk with their dog. Humans have their own views on what constitutes a nice walk, but your perception is what matters and you need to quickly impose your own discipline on the walking process.

Speed – If your human is too slow, feel free to indicate this by pulling on the lead. This is particularly an issue if you are a young dog with plenty of energy. Your human must be trained to keep up with you. Don't mind the moaning from behind about aching arms and being dragged along, just go at the pace that seems suitable to you and make them keep up. This is where a harness comes in handy as you can throw your whole weight into it without risking any unpleasantness to yourself. Sometimes people, in misguided attempts to get you to walk 'to heel' will try and employ fiendish devices such as the kind which pulls against your muzzle if you strain too hard at the lead. This kind of behaviour needs a swift and firm response. Make it as difficult to fit as possible in the first place by fidgeting and shaking your head. If this doesn't discourage such anti-sociable behaviour, immediately try and remove it using your paws, scratching repeatedly at the straps. If all else fails, grind to a halt and refuse to budge until it has been removed. I know this seems extreme, but it does usually work if you persist. Sometimes humans will have done some research and will have read things about turning and walking in the opposite direction if a dog is pulling, or stopping and waiting for them to halt too. The only way to deal with this wayward behaviour is to be strong willed. Usually your lead-bearer will have other activities they need to be getting on with in their day and there will only be so long allowed for their walk, so just be stubborn and wear them down, they'll give in eventually.

The opposite problem, particularly if you are a very small or senior dog, is a lead-bearer who tries to walk too quickly. They are also frequently uneducated in the importance for us dogs of sniffing. We need to know who else has been passed, their state of health and any other news they've got to impart. If we don't meet them in person, how else are we possibly going to find out? We need to have a good, long, lingering sniff so don't allow them to rush you. If they try and move on too quickly I personally favour the brace position, with my front paws planted firmly ahead and my weight thrown backwards. When they turn round to see what the problem is, you need to deploy the baleful stare. This is one of an important range of canine expressions that can be used to communicate your displeasure to people who don't speak dog, or only have a very limited understanding of some of the simpler commands. It combines looking affronted with looking slightly mistreated and is best administered with direct eye-contact. As soon as they desist and wait for you, reward them instantly with a happy expression so that they know they've done the correct thing.

Sometimes your lead-bearer may want to go a shorter or greater distance than you feel is necessary or go in a different direction to your preferred route. The answer to correcting these behaviours is to use the same tactics as for regulating the speed of the walk. Above all, you need to be tenacious and persistent. If you once start to give in, your lead-bearer will labour under the misapprehension that they are in charge which is something to be avoided at all costs.

Recall

One of the most important pieces of training to master in the early days is the prompt recall of your owner at the point when they are needed by you. If you are busy socialising with other dogs, chasing rabbits or squirrels, playing or just enjoying a good sniff, of course you won't need them. Sometimes, they may want you to come to them, but this is something you should do only if it's convenient for you. Make sure that they give you a biscuit when you deign to show up. 'Her Indoors' always gives me a treat if I come back the first time she asks and I insist on this. If, by any chance, she forgets, I might allow her the benefit of the doubt the first time; what can I tell you I'm a generous fur, but if she forgets a second time, I make sure I don't come back, just to make the point. Sometimes people can get a bit irritable if you don't return promptly, particularly if they're running to a schedule that involves work and school runs, but you don't want to worry about this. After all, what's the worst they can do? Sometimes they will come trotting after you in an effort to enforce their will, but even the youngest or most elderly dog can easily out-manoeuvre a person, so again, this really isn't a problem.

Sometimes people buy various devices to aid communication in the recall department, such as clickers, but the same applies to these as to simple shouting: only take notice if it suits you. People also buy those special dog whistles which apparently emit a sound that is so high pitched that only dogs can hear it. There is however a good reason why humans can't hear them: they don't work! It just shows how gullible people can be. They stand there blowing away with puffed out cheeks until they're quite red in the face, in the firm belief that they are summoning their canine companion. I generally ignore them but, just occasionally, I respond as if I can hear something, just to give them hope. It's actually quite amusing so I don't want to spoil the fun by allowing the truth to slowly dawn.

If you need your owner to come back to you, that of course is a different matter. If you are tired and want to go home, just stand still and eventually they'll amble over and attach the lead. If it's urgent you can always run back to them. They like this as it makes them feel important. The one time I always employ this tactic is if things get out of hand in the dog socialising department, then I'm back like a shot, hiding behind 'Her Indoors' legs. This stimulates her protective, mothering instinct, and she sorts out the problem without me getting too involved in the unpleasantness.

On one occasion, we were heading to the playing fields in the normal way, when two dogs appeared that we hadn't seen before. I don't know what breed they were but it definitely had the words 'bull' and 'terrier' somewhere in the title. Anyway, they didn't hang about and both set about me in a horribly determined fashion. I managed to get back to 'Her Indoors' and, if I say so myself, all those years of training really paid off. She could see I was in serious trouble so she ran at the dominant dog, screaming like a banshee. Then she remembered reading something about dogs being frightened of a suddenly opened umbrella, so she opened her golfing umbrella in its face. There may have been a little bit of foot work with her dog-walking boots too. There was one horrible moment, when we thought the dogs were going to start on her, but they thought better of it and ran back to their owner, defeated. 'Her Indoors' checked me all over for injuries as she thought I'd almost inevitably have been hurt, and then started to walk over the field to give their ineffectual owner a piece of her mind. The woman took one look at 'Her Indoors' in full sail, and immediately put both the dogs in the car, with her young toddler, and drove away. I don't know who was more shaken, me or 'Her Indoors', but we had to have a little sit down and a shared moment when we got home. We subsequently discovered that those same two dogs had once caught and killed a cat. As I'm not much bigger than a cat myself, I shudder to think what could have happened if I hadn't done my basic training with 'Her Indoors'.

I have to be honest however and acknowledge that even with my expertise it isn't always plain sailing. One day we were having our walk when a very large Rottweiler approached. I gave him the usual brisk terrier introduction, just to let him know from the outset, the natural pecking order, and I distinctly heard 'Her Indoors' mutter under her breath that if I upset this one, I was on my own. Bloomin' cheek! I like to think that she was doing a bit of terrier bluffing herself and that, if push had come to shove, she would have been in there, fighting my corner, but sometimes, even with the best training, doubt does start to creep in. Under those circumstances it's best to heed the warning signs and go back to basics. You can't afford to let things deteriorate on the training front.

Other Commands

There are a range of other commands that you might want to teach your human. One of the most important ones, in my opinion, is the giving of treats on command. My signal for a treat is to sit down, squarely in front of 'Her Indoors' and make determined eye contact. If this doesn't immediately elicit the required response, I pick up one paw and hold it in an imploring way, shaking slightly, as if about to pass out through inanition. This always has the desired response and a treat is forthcoming. I have perfected this art so well, that I have trained total strangers that I meet regularly whilst out walking, to perform the same role. I can even get them to give me more than one treat, but this is an advanced skill and you will need years of practise to get to this level. Some dogs like to give something back, in response, and will do things like sit, lie down, or get their owner to shake hands with them, but I find all this kind of training a bit superfluous to requirements. I only sit or lie down when I feel like it or when it's convenient to do so as I don't want 'Her Indoors' getting any incorrect notions about who is really in charge.

Training Classes

Sometimes people get some strange ideas about dogs needing to do as they are told, and, despite the best efforts of their canines who have ensured that their owner's own attempts to make this happen have proved unsuccessful, they then seek further help by taking their dog to training classes. If this happens with your owner, don't panic, there are a number of tactics that can be deployed.

Firstly, the best of these classes are run by people who understand that it isn't actually the dog who needs training, it's the owner. These trainers are usually women, middle-aged or older, who wear tweedy skirts and flat, sensible, lace-up shoes. They are often very stern with the owners and nice to the dogs, which is of course the correct way around. It's before my time but I have seen a few clips on the television of a woman of this type called Barbara Woodhouse, who used to put the fear of God into the lead-bearers. Often, if this happens, your human will be discouraged from going, but if they persist, the secret is to obey anything the trainer says instantly and consistently, and at the same time disregard anything your human asks you to do, that way the trainer will rightly conclude that the problem is with your owner rather than with you. Job done!

Sometimes however, the dog trainers are of the new-fangled dog psychologist type who will talk about things such as 'the pack order'. Of course there is some truth in these theories, it's just that the correct order has you at the top of it. There was a woman of this type, who used to wear a suspicious amount of black leather, and had a popular show on the television. It really makes you wonder at the responsibility or lack of it, of the broadcasters who allow this kind of erroneous nonsense to be shared with susceptible dog-owners, making our job as dogs, twice as hard. However, if you find yourself unwillingly at one of these classes, don't despair, help is at hand.

You have two possible lines of defence. The first, which is personally the one I would favour if I found myself in this unfortunate circumstance, is to be so naughty you get expelled from the class. This is quite simple to do and is actually quite good fun. Totally ignore everyone's commands, disrupt the class, argue with other dogs, set a bad example and lead others astray too, wee and pooh on the floor like a dog who has never heard of house training and just generally indulge yourself in whatever way you think fit. The only caveat is that you mustn't be responsible for anyone coming to actual harm, human or canine, but other than that, the way is clear.

If you are an amiable kind of dog and really can't bring yourself to do this, the second option is to go along with it, whilst at the class. Do everything you are told to do, in style and watch your owner bask in your reflected glory. They need to enjoy this whilst they can however. As soon as you are out of class, you just revert to normal and promptly forget everything you were told. Your human will be wringing their hands, telling disbelieving people repeatedly, how good you are in class and how they can't understand why you are behaving so badly once you are at home. You need to be consistent and eventually, even the most persistent offender will become demoralised and give up. Sorted!

Socialisation
One of the key areas for training is to ensure that your owner is properly socialised. Humans are, after all, pack animals, and need to be in the company of their own kind. As soon as you have had your vaccinations, if you are a puppy, or straight away if you are an adult dog, you need

to get your folk out there, meeting other people. You will provide a useful point of contact, allowing people to initiate conversation. This has many advantages. If the people are other dog owners or dog lovers, as is often the case, they will admire and make a fuss of you, possibly giving you treats, if you apply your training techniques effectively. Even if they are not doggy types, they will often get chatting and distract your owner so that you will get some 'me' time, to indulge in your own interests and amusements, without having to accommodate the sensibilities of your owner. This is all valuable stuff.

You do have to be a bit wary of other dog owners passing on tips and advice, particularly if your human has never been owned by a dog before, but if they do, hopefully that advice will directly contradict that given by someone else or in a book, so confusion will set in and you will be free to set your human on the correct track, uninhibited. If the person has their own dog with them, feel free to reciprocate and role model the correct behaviour for the other dog to follow; it's always good to have an audience. With a bit of luck, you will soon establish a reputation in your local area which can only be to the good.

One of the good things about meeting a range of different people is that it gives you the opportunity to expose your owner to a range of possible activities and events that you can do together. Now that you have mastered the basics, you can indulge in extra-curricular activities, and this is what we shall be talking about in the next chapter.

Chapter Five

Extra-curricular activities

Having covered the basic training with your owner, you should now be free to involve them in some extra-curricular activities for your mutual benefit.

Dog Shows
Some pooches like nothing better than to strut their stuff in the show ring, being admired and generally made a fuss of, and if this is something you want to be involved in, you need to get your human up to the mark.

Firstly, they need to realise that it's all about you; their role is very much secondary. So they need to groom you until your fur shines, make sure you are trim and that your teeth are gleaming, and ensure that you don't get too tired so that you've got plenty of energy left for the ring. They, on the other hand, will probably struggle to drag a comb through their hair or clean their own teeth as they'll be so busy looking after you. Whilst you will be on prime form, they may well be a bit jaded by the time the moment of judgement comes, but don't worry. A good judge will ignore a dishevelled owner and focus on the lovely canine so it shouldn't count against you. Dogs who have trained their human well, will often have them wearing an outfit in a complementary colour to their own coat, so that they are shown to best advantage. However, if your human is a complete numpty in the ring, you can always employ a professional handler to accompany you so you are not held back in your efforts to excel.

I haven't done much showing myself. If I'm entirely objective, I don't think I match my breed standard that well. We Border Terriers are supposed to have otter-shaped heads, although why that is when we're dogs not otters is beyond me, but my muzzle is quite pointed. I have found this very useful for getting into packets; if you've got a pointy nose you can get right into the corners, but I think it might count against me in the show ring. I also have another disadvantage: 'Her Indoors'. We had a go at the local, fun dog show and I'm disappointed to report that she didn't take it very seriously. She seemed to think it was all just a bit of a laugh and as for her trotting in the ring, well the least said about that the better.

Some dogs have the opposite problem and their owners can get very competitive and worked up about the whole thing. If this happens, you may need to put your paw down, after all, it's about you not them. The best way to do this is to make your feelings clear, in the ring. Good examples of this can be seen most years at Crufts. Do your own thing, stop to have a wee or even better, a quick pooh, lie down, get distracted, the choice quite frankly is endless. And if you want to go off-piste and follow your own inclination that's fine too. A really good example of this was a rescue Jack Russell called Ollie, who was competing in an agility class. After a promising start, he nose-dived over one of the jumps. Untroubled by this, he decided against weaving in and out of those little poles and took the direct route. He then went through the tunnel starting at the wrong end, ran up the 'A' frame with such vigour that all four paws left the frame over the apex, which he celebrated with a little backward kick, and then he wandered off to greet his admiring fans close-up. Having received their homage, he decided that the collecting ring was more interesting than the show arena and exited stage left with his owner running to catch up behind him. She had clearly been well trained by Ollie as she was taking it in good part which was nice to see.

At some dog shows there are fun activities for dogs to take part in. One year I participated in a competition for the fastest dog. There was a fenced off running lane with one person at the far end to stop you setting off too early, and your owner at the other, encouraging you to run to them. The secret here, is to train your owner into making coming to them as appealing as possible, so you are not distracted by the waft of cooking hotdogs or a game that involves chasing a rat down a drain pipe. The first time we did it, 'Her Indoors' was a bit luke-warm about encouraging me, but as it was the best of three, she soon got into school sports day mode and was yelling at me like her life depended on it. Encouraged, I ran a bit quicker and managed quite a commendable time for a senior dog. The winner, rather predictably, was a whippet. They've got a bit of an advantage in the speed department and make the rest of us look like we're just trotting. Still, it's the taking part that counts and I have to say it was a lot of fun.

Another thing that is good fun, if you get the chance and are of the correct disposition, is terrier racing. It's a bit like greyhound racing but on a smaller scale and isn't taken as seriously, or at least it hasn't been on the occasions I've experienced it. The terriers are all placed in starting gates and when they are released, they chase after a fluffy lure, a bit like a squirrel or a rabbit, and the winner is the one who gets down the track quickest. As we terriers are rather vocal when we're excited, and even when we're not to be honest, it tends to be quite noisy. The only training you have to do of your owner is for them to yell encouragement and get over excited, which, to be frank, is quite easily achieved for all but the most placid. If you've got a shy and retiring human you might think this isn't an activity for them but you couldn't be more wrong from my experience. It can stir up the competitive urge in even the quietest person, with raucous shouting and even the odd expletive. Try and be tolerant, after all, it does them good to let off a bit of steam.

The first time I witnessed this activity close-up, was when we went to a regional Border Terrier get together, to which I had been invited to promote my previous book, *The Last Rolo*. 'Her Indoors' was concerned about me aggravating my arthritis, and I didn't have the heart to worry her, she gets very anxious now I'm a senior, so I didn't take part. But I watched from the sidelines and it looked great fun. On this particular occasion, the person operating the lure, misjudged the speed of the terriers and the dogs managed to catch it. They all piled in joyously but when they were required to release it so that the race could be restarted, they held on tenaciously and developed it into a game of terrier tugging. It's amazing that the lure was in any fit state to resume its duties as a target, but they did eventually manage to get the event back on track, if you'll excuse the pun.

Charitable Work

Some dogs, of a generous disposition, like to get involved in good deeds, and also train their owners to actively participate, which is always nice to see. Sometimes it can be something simple like a sponsored dog walk which has the added advantages of being good fun and keeping your humans fit and well socialised. The other year I did one for BBC Children in Need. As I'm a family dog, I've always had a soft spot for juniors, so it was an obvious charity for me to support. I have to say 'Her Indoors' stepped up to the mark pretty well. She bought some spotted material like Pudsey's bandage, and made some bandanas for participating furs. Although she did her best, the stitching didn't stand close inspection and they all came up slightly different sizes, but as Border Terriers vary quite a bit too, this didn't really matter, she just matched the bandana to the dog. Anyway, we managed to raise a respectable donation.

The Twitter group that I belong to, the BT Posse, supports our own, Border Terrier charity, Border Terrier Welfare. This is a great charity that re-homes Border Terriers who, for all kinds of good reasons, need new homes. Every year the BT Posse produces its own calendar that it sells to raise money for BTW and I have been one of the featured dogs for several years on the trot. The first year I was Mr May, and was tastefully caught in an action pose, playing with a tennis ball in the garden, my ears flying happily in the breeze, wearing just a bandana – anything for charity! This year I'm shown in a literary pose, reading one of my own books, demonstrating the intellectual capacity of our breed, should anyone be in any doubt. Whilst us Border Terriers are clearly the stars of the show, a few get their folks involved in putting the calendar together and distributing it and the rest of us get our people to buy them, after all, what else do they go to work for?

Having mastered the basic training of charitable giving with 'Her Indoors', I'm pleased to say that she's moved onto a more advanced level. There's a charity called the Cinnamon Trust that helps out dogs whose owners are ill or elderly and can no longer walk them. These dogs are so devoted to their owners that they won't allow themselves to be re-homed and this is where the charity steps in, providing dog walkers to regularly assist. 'Her Indoors' discovered that there was one such situation in our neighbourhood so she applied to be a volunteer dog walker. The security clearance is similar to working for MI5, but, as I've generally managed to keep her out of any serious trouble over the years, she was eventually approved and now takes a couple of dogs out on a regular basis. I like to feel that my good training has paid off and that other dogs are now benefitting from the considerable efforts I have put in with 'Her Indoors'.

Pets as Therapy

Some particularly altruistic dogs, like to get involved in visiting people in hospital, schools and retirement homes, spreading the benefit of canine company to those who are sadly deprived of such affections. If you want to do this kind of work, you first need to do an honest appraisal of your owner. You need to ask yourself the following questions:

- Are they the kind of person who doesn't mind you sharing your affections with complete strangers or are they the jealous type?

- Do they get on well with a variety of different people of various ages and from a variety of different backgrounds? If helping with junior reading is likely to make them want to hang themselves from the Oxford Reading Tree then this clearly isn't the role for them.

- Are they able to cope in unfamiliar environments such as hospitals and hospices? For some people, the overwhelming smell of disinfectant and the reflected gleam from the floors is just too much. Also, you occasionally get an owner who has had a distressing experience in a medical setting, like being told to lose weight, cut down on their units or do more exercise, and this will affect their reactions in similar settings in the future. You need to be sensitive to this.

- Also, are they prepared to put in the necessary time to get through the approval process and are they then prepared to be seen with a pooch wearing a bright yellow coat? Could they be

persuaded to wear the matching T-Shirt? You
need to think of these things.

These are all important considerations and it's no good
trying to get your owner to do this if they are, in reality, a
Victor Meldrew type who just wants to be left alone to
watch the TV.

Gardening
Some dogs have very specific leisure interests that they
like to involve their humans in. Gardening is a case in
point. I enjoy a bit of quality outside time with my family
and I'm certainly not alone in that. Look at Monty Don
and his Golden Retrievers Nigel and Nellie. Monty
probably thinks that people tune in to watch his
gardening tips and admire the plants, but the truth is
they're waiting with bated breath to see what the dogs get
up to each week. This is perfectly understandable and is
due to the nation's dogs carefully training their owners.

If you like gardening and want your owners to be
involved, you need to train them specifically. Give them
the signal that you want to go outside, but when they
open the back door, stand and look forlornly at them so
that they have to come outside with you. If the garden is
looking a bit overgrown or weedy, lose your ball in the
undergrowth and then whine piteously so that they have
to help you find it. Repeat this persistently until they get
fed up with scratches and nettle stings and clear the
weeds away. If you think a bit of digging is needed, just
get in there and set them an example. You don't need to
worry about what other plants may be there, after all it
can sometimes be difficult to tell which are plants and

which are weeds, just dig and if you've got it wrong the cry of anguish from your owner and the choice language will give you a little clue.

Some dogs like flowers and find them comfy to lie on, particularly when they're in full bloom and looking especially lovely. Crushing them can often help with the release of fragrance as well as giving a good insulating layer between you and the ground, so if you like that kind of thing, encourage your humans to grow some. I personally have a preference for vegetable and fruit growing. There's nothing nicer than fresh, home grown produce and I like to have a little wander, helping myself as I go. Strawberries are a particular favourite. I had a little bit of trouble in the sharing department initially. 'Them Indoors' seemed to think that they were entitled to the soft fruit and in the beginning the birds got the blame for any little absences until I was caught in a compromising position with my head in the strawberry patch. To start with, they tried to ban me from the plot, but I wasn't having any of that and persisted. Now, I am given any that have blemishes or that the birds have genuinely had a peck at, whilst 'Them Indoors', who are far more fussy about what their food looks like, consume the rest. It's probably a bit soft-hearted of me and you might want to be firmer with your own family, but I sometimes think a compromise is in the best interests of domestic harmony.

Greenhouses are also a good thing to encourage your owners to take an interest in. Not only do they provide one big sun-puddling spot, especially on days in the spring and autumn when there's a cool breeze blowing outside, but they can also be used for growing a whole new range of delicious treats like tomatoes. You can help yourself to them, if you are so inclined, in the same way as other soft fruit, only just make sure you don't confuse them with the chilli plants, whose fruit are often the same colour, otherwise you'll be the first jet-propelled dog in space.

Cycling
There has also been an increased interest in cycling over recent years, due at least in part, to our success as a country in national cycling competitions. If you are keen on sports cycling you can supervise their efforts by running alongside the bike and setting a brisk pace to ensure there's no slacking. Good training will ensure that somewhere in one of those cycling pockets will be some edibles and a drink, not for the cyclist – they can wait until they get home – but for their canine trainer. It's best to build up the distance gradually, you don't want your owner putting a strain on their joints, but you can create a happy cycling partnership that both of you can enjoy.

Some cycling pursuits are a little more sedentary. 'Her Indoors' has got a sensible bike with a sturdy frame and a large basket on the front which she mistakenly seemed to think was for her shopping. It's taken a while, but now she realises that it is, in fact, the ideal cycling transportation for a small dog. I wear a harness that fastens me in for safety's sake. 'Her Indoors' has a cycle helmet which, after years of nagging the juniors to wear when they were out cycling, she tries to avoid wearing herself if she can possibly get away with it. True, it does make her look like an animated lollipop on a rather large stick, and gives her a nasty case of helmet hair with a fetching buckle imprint on her left cheek, but at her age, she really doesn't have to worry about her looks. I don't have any concerns about my appearance; I like a bit of wind through my fur, and us Border Terriers are supposed to look scruffy and rugged, it's part of our considerable appeal. Anyway, she puffs along, stopping to walk up the hills, whilst I sit happily, enjoying the view and commenting on the surrounding countryside, animals, people and dogs, whenever I think fit. We live in the countryside so we tend to cycle down the quiet lanes as cars zooming past too close can be a bit unnerving for both of us.

If you are a larger pooch and won't fit in a basket, don't despair, there are bicycle side cars and trailers for dogs which look great fun. I haven't tried one myself although I'd like to, but you have your own little chariot, a bit like the ones that are used for very young juniors, and you can cycle along in luxury, with a nice hood to keep you dry or in the shade depending on the weather conditions.

Pub Dogs
Some pooches train their owners in the art of running a pub which is a fine thing. The combination of people in a sociable mood, food and beer, often alongside a nice pub garden in the summer and a roaring fire in the winter, provides a perfect habitat for most dogs. It does however have its draw backs. You have to be prepared to share your home with all and sundry, including other dogs who may or may not be to your liking, you have to listen with attention to some sometimes frankly dull and length anecdotes, plus you have to be able to deal patiently with

inebriated people without resorting to giving them the bite on the bum that so many of them amply deserve. You also have to work long and anti-social hours with very little time off.

In one of our local pubs, there's a Springer Spaniel who serves behind the bar, supervising his humans and living up to his name, jumping up, with his front paws on the counter, so that people can stroke and make a fuss of him. His owners are well-socialised, patient, friendly and hard-working so he's obviously trained them well, but to be honest, it's not for everyone.

For many, the best solution is to take your owners along to the pub as an occasional treat. Some discerning pubs seem to actually prefer dogs to people as they offer free canine drinks and food, whilst making their accompanying owners pay for theirs. I suspect this is the result of very specific training by pub dogs and is to be applauded and encouraged. However, if it is the kind of pub that seems to be more geared up to people than pooches, you need to make it clear, right from the outset, that no trip to the pub is complete without a little snack or the odd chip so deploy your hungry eyes without restraint. If you are ambitious, you might succeed in getting little snacks from other people too. Just look at them as if you haven't had a square meal for at least a week and whimper, that usually does it.

Television and Radio
It's good to encourage your family to take an interest in the outside world. How else are they going to find out about important developments such as medical advances for dogs, our history, and some kind of understanding

about our behaviours, although they are never truly going to get there on that one, bless them. There are, of course, a few ground rules however that need setting from the beginning.

The television belongs to you, not them, and you need to choose the channels. Some dogs struggle with this but it's really quite easy. If the programme is not to your liking, try yawning repeatedly. This works particularly well if you are up close and personal, and even better, if you are a little challenged in the halitosis department. If this doesn't work, try some other techniques such as whining loudly, barking directly at the television, or playing with a toy so noisily that it drowns out the sound. If none of these tactics work, you could always try a few well-timed emissions. The only danger with this is that you run the risk of being banished on health and safety grounds. Once the message has finally got through, reward your human by watching very attentively, moving to a close-up position in front of the screen, so that they are left in no doubt about the kind of programme you best enjoy. Don't worry if sitting in front blocks their view, this just serves to reinforce whose television it is anyway, and they can always move.

When viewing the television, you will need to ensure that your owners understand the importance of giving you the best viewing position. You might find lying on the sofa is most comfortable, or, like me, you might want to monopolise your own viewing platform such as my bean bag in the lounge. Whatever works for you, make sure that your family accommodate your needs and not the other way around.

Another form of home entertainment that you might want to train your family into arranging for your convenience is the radio. Getting the correct station is similar to getting the correct programme on the television. I'm a Radio Four dog myself so we tend to have that on all the time in the kitchen. I think 'Them Indoors' benefit from having their minds improved and it is important, as owners get older, to keep them sufficiently mentally challenged as this has been shown to decrease the chances of them developing illnesses such as Alzheimer's – I don't want them forgetting my meals any more than they do now, thank you very much. I have however, trained them to switch to something livelier when there are fireworks going off nearby. It isn't so bad now that I'm a senior and a bit deaf, but when I was younger, I used to find them very distressing to my sensitive hearing and the music used to drown them out. I have to say, in fairness, that they caught on very quickly after I'd shared my distress at full volume.

You can also train your humans in a similar way, to leave the radio on for you if they should venture out without you. Sometimes you'll need your staff to go out and do boring things like getting the car serviced, that you won't want to be bothered with, so you can lie in your bed at home instead, and catch up on what's going on in the world. After all, there might be some new extracurricular activities that are becoming popular and that you might want to train your humans to participate in, so you need to make sure that you remain well-informed.

Chapter Six

Health and Well-being

Most owners will naturally want what is best for you, but you need to ensure that you keep them up to the mark in the on-going routine healthcare and well-being department as these things can be inadvertently forgotten in the bustle of everyday life.

Routine Health and Vaccination Appointments
If you have chosen your Vets well, you won't need to do any training in your owner remembering to make regular health check appointments; the Vet will do it for you with little reminder cards that they send in the mail. If you are of a post-shredding disposition, it is probably best to leave this one unscathed. In fact, if there's any danger of it being overlooked, you can always move it to the top of

the pile that way you can ensure that your health needs are fully and promptly met.

They are varying approaches to ensure that you get the maximum overall benefit from these appointments. Some dogs decide from an early age to manifest a strong dislike of the Vet's and have to be dragged and cajoled out of cars, across the car park and over the threshold. I've seen some really good performances over the years, particularly from large dogs, who have to be pushed through the doorway, quaking, with their ears down, looking the epitome of misery. Vet's surgeries usually have shiny floors and this is not just for reasons of cleanliness. It also makes it more difficult for dog's claws to get a grip and it's easy to push a reluctant canine, whilst in a sitting or reclined position, as they slide more easily across the floor.

Now of course, most of this reluctance is for show and demonstrates good training by the dogs in question. If they appear frightened they get much more in the way of sympathy and treats than a dog who breezes in happily, apparently unconcerned. It's one of my own areas for development; I've been far too obliging in this matter, but I like to think I make up for it by the deployment of my hungry eyes during the consultation.

You also need to train your owner as far as the conduct of the examinations and vaccinations are concerned. I don't mind injections. To be honest, I don't really feel them so find it difficult to time a convincing reaction. However, I don't like the kennel cough vaccination as they squirt it up your nose – who would. I've therefore made it clear to 'Her Indoors' and to the Vet that the only way I am going to cooperate is with the aid of a large chew. 'Her Indoors' hangs on grimly to one end whilst I hang on equally grimly to the other. Whilst this is going on, the Vet nips in quick and squirts the vaccine up my nose. I then give a big sneeze and spray it all over them, so that their immune systems are boosted too; what can I tell you I'm a generous fur, and then I get the whole chew to finish off. Sorted!

'Her Indoors' tries to get maximum benefit from my annual health check by squeezing in as many concerns and minor ailments as possible, but I find that if you're working up to being ill, it's best to hide symptoms at these consultations and save them to prompt a separate visit only a few days later. That way you double the treats and get more attention for individual problems. After all, what else have they got to spend their money on?

Health Insurance

As there isn't a National Health Service for dogs yet, you may want to get your family to take out private health insurance on your behalf. They might want to wait months for appointments and hang around for hours in crowded waiting rooms with frazzled receptionists in Victorian buildings, but it should be gleaming white porcelain, attractive nurses in smart uniforms, and tasteful décor for you. Also, a good insurance policy will provide cover for any other little mishaps that might occur that your owners would be legally liable for.

Who to get cover with is a difficult issue as there are a wide variety of providers out there. You can be sure however, that whichever one you choose, will increase the premiums significantly as you get older, and the likelihood of you needing to claim increases, and heaven help you if you do actually claim, your premiums will shoot through the roof and a whole string of extra terms and conditions will be imposed the next time you renew. It's generally better to avoid claiming at all, something insurance companies actively encourage. Make sure that treatment for any minor ailments costs slightly less or the same as the compulsory excess on your policy. If something major needs doing, make sure that it is on the list of exclusions, or if you really have to claim, ensure that you exceed the maximum limit payable for anyone condition, so that your owners have to pay up anyway. It's a good way of reminding your family that you are far more important to them than a new car or a holiday abroad.

General Maintenance
In addition to your health needs, there are certain things that require doing on a regular basis, and you should train your family to suitably prioritise your needs above other, less important activities.

Grooming – All dogs, regardless of type, need regular grooming. If you are a breed with a long or particularly dense coat, you will need frequent attention and you need to make sure that your owner gets the brush out on a regular basis, from the early days, so that good habits are established. You need to make sure that your coat is comfortable, clean, and you are looking your best.

We Border Terriers have two coats: a fine fluffy layer close to the skin to keep us warm; a kind of woolly vest, and a harsh overcoat that protects us from the weather. In order to keep it looking good we undergo a process called 'hand stripping' which basically involves pulling the old coat out. It is easy to let your owner know when this needs doing as you just develop an appearance reminiscent of an Ewok on a bad hair day, and peer out from under your fringe. It's best to time grooming for just before a cold spell, so that when you emerge looking like a newly shorn sheep, your owner is overcome with guilt and buys you new coats and warm bedding to make up for your lack of an insulating layer.

Whatever your coat type, feel free, when the weather is hot, to shed your fur freely. Don't worry if your breed type is described as 'non-shedding'; it's too late now and although my knowledge of consumer law is a bit vague, I'm pretty sure it doesn't apply to the shedding proclivities of varying dog breeds, so they can't take you back and demand a refund. No, they'll just have to get the vacuum cleaner out and be grateful for the exercise. It's either that or tolerate great balls of dead fur blowing around the house like tumble weed.

Bathing – This is closely associated with grooming and there are varying views on this within the canine world. Like Marmite, some love it and some of us hate it.

If, like me, you are a dog who doesn't like to get wet, then you need to train your humans into bathing you as infrequently as possible. You can achieve this by following a few simple steps:

- Learn the warning signs that a bath is imminent. In my case this usually involves more moaning than normal from 'Him Indoors' with the frequent use of such words as 'pongy', 'wiffy' and 'fleabag'. Also watch out for the gathering of equipment which, for me, is a baby bath in the winter and a watering can in the summer. The latter is difficult as it is usually associated with watering the garden, an activity that I enjoy, so you need to watch out for secondary signs such as shampoo gathering, and, in my case, a long lead being sourced to fasten me to the Walnut tree in the garden so I cannot escape. 'Her Indoors' often wears an apron and rubber gloves, so I keep a wary eye open for those too.

- Run away! A simple but direct and highly effective tactic. After all, you are significantly faster than them and they'll soon loose heart.

- Adopt the brace position. This only really works if you are a large dog; if I do it 'Her Indoors' just picks me up. Make it as difficult as possible for them to manoeuvre you to the required location.

- Inevitably, you will eventually be caught – people can be quite cunning, what can I tell you – so look as miserable as possible during the whole process. Droop your ears and tail, shiver so that they worry you are catching a chill and look hungry. When your coat is wet you'll suddenly seem a lot smaller and thinner than you normally do so use this to your advantage.

- Make as much mess as possible. Wait until you are fully lathered up with shampoo and then shake and see how far you can get those muddy, soapy droplets to travel. I aim to ensure the whole bathroom needs a clean if 'Her Indoors' is washing me inside, that way she thinks twice before subjecting me to the whole sordid business. It's a bit trickier when she does it out in the garden but then my aim is to get as much of it over 'Her Indoors' as I possibly can.

- When it's over, at the earliest opportunity, find something to roll in. This has the advantage of getting rid of that horrible perfumed smell that accompanies a bath, and also demonstrates the futility of the process.

If you follow this advice you will significantly reduce the number of times you are bathed. As a result of my careful training, 'Her Indoors' has purchased some dry shampoo that she sprinkles all over my coat and then brushes it out. I still end up smelling like a powder puff but at least I don't have to get wet. If, of course, you like being bathed then ignore all the above advice and relish the attention.

Claw clipping – Dogs who are regularly exercised on hard surfaces, don't generally need their claws clipping, they wear down naturally. However, dogs who are exercised on softer surfaces such as grass, or senior dogs who don't do as much walking as they used to, can need a quick trim every now and then.

It's easy to let your owner know when they need doing. Just find a hard surface and click them like castanets. That should do the trick. Ideally, they need to take you to a groomer or to the Vets to get them cut. It's not that they do a better job, it's just that they charge more which proves how valuable an asset you are to the household. If your owner is tempted to try a bit of DIY in the dog maintenance department, make sure they have the proper tools and that they read up on the subject first. We dogs have a living part to our claws, just like the pink bit of their finger nails, and if they cut into that it is both painful and bloody. Should the worst happen, you need to play the situation to your advantage. Yelp, howl, shake, bleed, limp, repeat! You should get new treats, new toys, and lots of love, plus they'll never dare to do it themselves again.

Teeth cleaning – Over recent years, it has become increasingly widely advised for owners to clean their dog's teeth on a regular basis as it reduces gum disease, bad breath and tooth decay. You need to decide whether you are in favour of this and then train your human accordingly. There are some advantages to teeth cleaning. It doesn't hurt and the toothpaste is often pleasantly flavoured according to likely canine preferences. You will also feel all minty fresh once the task has been completed and are more likely to be allowed to get up close and personal with your family.

I don't approve of teeth cleaning. I don't want 'Her Indoors' poking around in my mouth thank you very much. I can therefore recommend some simple training techniques to ensure this doesn't happen. Firstly, keep your mouth shut! There's no way they can get a tooth brush in then. However, if they are very persistent and wait until you open your mouth, clamp down hard on the bristle end and hang on like your life depends on it. Most dogs are very good at playing tug so just ignore the increasingly shrill commands to 'Drop, DROP!', and refuse to let go. After a prolonged spell of this, your owner won't venture to try again.

However, I do realise the importance of ensuring that my mouth is in a healthy state, after all, I use it for a lot of things, so I've trained 'Her Indoors' to provide me with those chews that clean your teeth as you eat them, that way you get a treat too. Job done!

Eye and ear cleansing – depending on your breed and age, you might need additional attention to your eyes and ears. As a senior dog, my eyes don't clean themselves quite as well as they did when I was younger and I get eye bogies at their corners. They don't really bother me and I'm quite happy to clean them myself with my paw, but sometimes, if I want to look especially smart for any reason, I get 'Her Indoors' to clean them. She uses a little piece of damp kitchen roll and I must say she is very gentle when she does it, so I just relish the attention and let her get on with it. But perhaps my favourite way of resolving this problem is when I'm in the lounge of an evening. I find that rubbing my face on the cream carpet or the rug, first one side and then the other, does the job wonderfully. 'Him Indoors' seems to find this very irritating – I can't think why- and usually moans at me. I just ignore him. What else are carpets and rugs for?

De-fleaing and worming – It is a harsh reality that we dogs occasionally play host to some unwelcome stowaways, so you need to train your humans to regularly administer drops and tablets to deal with the little critters. If they need reminding, just do plenty of vigorous scratching, and that should serve the purpose. Flea drops are usually administered to the back of the neck and shoulders so that we can't reach to lick it off which is a bit of a shame. I wonder what it tastes like?

Worming tablets are served up with your food. I'm afraid my naturally hungry disposition has prevented me from maximising the potential of this little undertaking. If it goes in my bowl, I eat it, no questions asked. However, some dogs refuse point blank to eat them and carefully remove all the surrounding food, leaving the tablet untouched. I admire their self-discipline as this leads to their owners trying to hide the tablets in delicious treats such as chicken or lumps of cheese. Again, if you've got the self-restraint, persist, and only eat the chicken or cheese, leaving the tablet intact. I heard of one dog who had perfected this training to such a pitch that he would only take his worming tablet if it was hidden in a piece of steak. Now that's what I call training!

Minor Ailments
However well you have trained your humans to look after you, there will be times, inevitably, that you succumb to illness. Now so far, I've been an extremely healthy dog, so my advice in this section will, necessarily be quite brief, but once you've mastered the basic principles, you can apply them to a whole range of issues.

Stomach upsets – I've always had an 'eat first, think later' policy on the basis that if it's something inedible, it usually finds its own way out, one end or the other. If it needs some assistance, I find eating grass and other associated foliage, helps to induce a suitable cleansing of the system. It is important that if you do this indoors, you time it just right. Wait until your owner is in another part of the house but still just within hearing range and then start, noisily retching. Build up to a crescendo as your owner comes running, and time it so that they arrive just at the moment when you finally succeed in bringing up whatever has been irritating you. You don't want them arriving too early otherwise you will be ignominiously shoved out of the back door. They can then offer you sympathy and clean up after you, which is only right and proper.

Occasionally, you will develop a proper stomach bug that results in you being betrayed by one or other end, and occasionally in severe cases, both. If this happens, don't worry, your owner will be on hand to look after you. You will be feeling pretty miserable so make sure that you share the pain with your family. If they put newspaper down at the back door, try to avoid using it. There's nothing worse than the smell of newsprint when you're feeling off colour, and why would you want to use that when you've got the entire kitchen floor and your bedding to choose from.

Foreign bodies – This isn't a reference to the kind of people UKIP object to, but the presence of items on your person that shouldn't really be there. I've had a few punctures in the paw department in my time and I've trained 'Her Indoors' to deal with them promptly and effectively. I'm quite a hardy soul so when I start limping, 'Her Indoors' know that there really is something the matter and that I'm not just faking it for attention, although this is an entirely appropriate tactic if you feel you are not getting your fair share of fuss. As I'm a relatively small dog, she just upends me in her lap and does a thorough examination of each foot, looking closely at each pad and in between, in case something sharp has got wedged. She then removes it promptly and I'm back to regular. Sometimes, in resolving our minor difficulties, our owners have to do something that is painful, but I've learnt over the years to be tolerant of this as me and 'Her Indoors' have a relationship of trust. I know she is trying to help and although, if it is incredibly painful I might curl my lip or give a slight rumble, it's only a token protest. She usually just curls her lip and rumbles back so that we retain a clear understanding of our relative feelings.

Eye/Ear infections – Sometimes dogs, like people, develop eye or ear infections and require treatment with drops. Administering drops is quite a skill and it is your job as a dog to make this as difficult as possible for your owner. Setting them little challenges keep them mentally stimulated and it also gives them an opportunity to try out some of the more choice words and phrases in their vocabulary. Beware of them trying to sneak up on you when you are sleeping and your guard is down. This kind of low tactic needs firmly rebuffing. Instead, try and ensure that your compliance is only bought by the generous application of treats. I've trained 'Them Indoors' to both get involved in the process. 'Him Indoors' acts as a kind of decoy, waving treats around in front of my nose whilst 'Her Indoors' hovers close by, waiting to swoop in the moment I'm distracted. Sometimes it gets a bit grumpy but keep your patience with them and remember, however inept they are, they are trying to help.

Urinary infections – Now I've never had one of these although I'm tempted to try as the idea of training 'Her

Indoors' to trot around the garden with a little plastic tray, trying to get a sample of my wee, is quite appealing.

Ticks – If you train your owner to use a good quality repellent, you shouldn't be unduly bothered by these little blighters, sucking your life blood, but unfortunately for us, 'Her Indoors' is clearly extremely tasty to anything in the insect department and she has had a few tick bites herself. Perhaps she should dab something between her shoulder blades and on the back of her neck. For her, the solution is to wear walking boots that cover her ankles and to lace them firmly over the bottom of her jeans so that ticks cannot crawl up. If you are unfortunate enough to be troubled with ticks, you will need to get your owner to remove them. Some people recommend a hot match being applied to the tick to shock it into releasing its grip. Another interesting recommendation is to apply a drop of gin with the same intention, although I suspect it just makes the tick too drunk to hold on. You can also buy special tick removers. However it is done, the important thing is that you remove the mouth parts otherwise you'll get an infection.

Wasp and bee stings – Despite 'Them Indoors' best efforts, I always chase wasps and bees, snapping at them once I'm within range. I'm not as accurate as I used to be; what can I tell you, my eyesight isn't as sharp as it once was, but occasionally I do get stung. This seems to distress 'Her Indoors' more than it does me. I just paw at the affected area for a bit and then resume my snapping. I think 'Her Indoors' forgets that I've got a good layer of fur so they don't generally hurt me as much as they hurt her. I remember one time when a wasp crawled into her sandal and she was stung on her instep. She was hopping around the hall swearing and her foot came up like a balloon. Still, stings are not a good in any quantity, so if you have an argument with more than one or two bees or wasps, it's as well to get your owner to seek medical advice.

Snake bites – Now I've never actually been bitten by a snake but that hasn't been through lack of trying. I have always hunted snakes in the garden, down in the nettles and the compost heap, and I've caught them quite a few times, but they've always been grass snakes. Although they don't bite they do squirt a foul-smelling liquid which is an irritant, so I've had to train 'Her Indoors' in the appropriate first aid which involves gently washing my face with warm water, although I've noticed that she tends to be less sympathetic than she was the first time. Adders are a very different matter and if you get bitten by one of those you need to go straight to the Vet as a matter of urgency. It's important to train your family to recognise the difference, otherwise you could be whisked to the Vet unnecessarily. Grass snakes vary a bit in colour but they have a white collar around their necks just below the head. Adders have a very definite zig zag along the top of their backs, unless they're black ones, which are…well…black, so you should be able to tell them apart. Having trained my family, with regard to snakes, they finally got tired of prizing them out of my jaws, and have cut down the nettles and fenced in the compost heap which has rather spoilt a bit of harmless fun. Just occasionally my family have a sense of humour failure.

Heat exhaustion – Every summer there are horrible stories of dogs being left in cars by poorly trained owners, and subsequently dying of heat exhaustion. People seem to think that if they park in the shade, leave a window ajar, and put some water out, that everything will be okay. It will not and you should protest loud and long if you find yourself in this situation. Bark as if your life depends on it as it may well do, and hopefully some better trained people will come along and smash a window to get you out. That will serve such negligent people right and will hopefully stop them from repeating such dangerous behaviour again.

Of course, this has never happened to me. Although 'Them Indoors' aren't perfect, they would never be that irresponsible. I did however suffer from the heat one day when I was a youngster and we went for a long walk. The way to train your owner into more a more considerate pattern of behaviour is to grind to a complete stop. In my case, 'Her Indoors' had to carry me until we came to a nice cool stream where I could have a paddle and a drink, and then I was okay to continue. Although I'm a small dog, 'Her Indoors' found me surprisingly heavy after carrying me for a while and we have a good photo of her looking hot and grumpy, carrying me, smiling and with my tongue lolling out. You've got to be firm sometimes.

Breed Specific Issues
Sometimes different breeds of dog have specific issues. Border Terrier are generally quite hardy so we are not specifically bothered, but you will need to ensure that your owners are correctly trained to meet your particular

needs. Spaniels, for instance, have long ears that need a bit of maintenance. Whilst you could probably take care of a lot of this yourself, why should you? That's what you have staff for. Another example comes with the giant breeds such as Great Danes and Irish Wolfhounds. They should not have too much exercise as it places an unnecessary strain on them. If you happen to be a large dog, and your owners are ill-informed, just grind to a halt when you're out on a walk. There is no way they'll be able to carry you or even move you, so it should be an effective way of getting the message home.

It is important that, whatever your breed, your owners are fully conversant with any specific problems you might encounter, so ensure that they do some appropriate research or ask the Vet so that they can fulfil their basic duty of ensuring that you are fit and well.

Chapter Seven

Life Events

Sometimes, even with the most careful training and care, things will not work out quite as you intended at the outset, so you need to be prepared to take the rough with the smooth. There are however, a few things that you can do that will help you through life's difficulties.

Divorce
Now this is not something I've had personal experience of yet, as 'Them Indoors' have been married for about a hundred years and generally seem to rub along okay. In fact, often when they do argue, I'm at the bottom of it in some shape or form, which is quite a proud achievement if you consider it in the right light. However, it is a harsh

fact that one in three marriages ends in divorce, so you need to know how to cope if the worst should happen.

There is a school of thought which suggests that you should not take sides in matrimonial disputes and that you should just stay patiently in the wings, waiting for them to sort it out for themselves. I do not agree. As I mentioned at the outset, every dog has their owner and, ideally you need to follow yours. It might be that there are other factors to consider, for example, if you're a family dog, you might want to have the same arrangements as your juniors. From my observations however, the problems seem to arise for dogs, when the change in family circumstances influences your owner's ability to care for you properly and it might be that you need to consider new care arrangements. Often however, after a period of stress and upheaval, you will find that things settle down into a new routine that works just as well, albeit differently to how things were before. Remember that all your family will need extra love and affection from you during this difficult time, but that if they have been well trained, they should continue to put your needs first.

Babies

If you have chosen a couple as your owners who are of breeding age, don't be surprised if they suddenly coyly announce that you are getting a little 'brother or sister'. Whilst this might come as a bit of a shock initially, particularly if they have said they didn't want children, it takes nine months to grown a human baby; they're quite slow at most things and this is no exception, so you've got a bit of time to get used to the idea.

I personally see juniors as a blessing. What better training opportunity is there for a dog, than to get a newly minted human, without any previous prejudices or poor experiences, and train them into being a dog loving person right from the outset? Whilst you might, quite rightly, be used to being the centre of the universe, there is no reason why, with the correct approach, you cannot continue to be a very important focus for your family even with a new junior, and I have witnessed many dogs successfully train their humans into making this transition.

During the pregnancy, you can offer support with morning sickness by eating any unwanted food, and with dietary fads by setting a good example. After all, you will have spent a life time consuming things that are not strictly edible, so if she develops a taste for something odd, you can be right there, beside her, making her feel that it's all perfectly normal. If she wants extra rest, you can kip with her, although if you normally snooze on her lap you might find yourself temporarily squeezed out, but don't worry, this doesn't have to be a metaphor for life in general. When they buy things for the baby, you can test them. Babies are big on chewing so if the equipment can stand your investigations it should be up to the mark. There will be bouncy chairs to try, mats to lie on and a pram/pushchair to purchase. You need to make sure they get a rugged one so that the new addition can accompany you on your walks right from the beginning. It might also be helpful to persuade your hupeeps into buying a front and/or back carrier as these are ideal for dog walkers as their hands remain free to tend to your needs.

As the big day approaches, don't be nervous. Babies are just a loud noise at one end and no sense of responsibility at the other; a bit like dogs in fact, so you're bound to get along. When they do arrive, there will inevitably be some disruption to your routine but just be stoical; things will settle down again very soon. There may be sleepless nights and noisy crying; babies can be quite troublesome too, but we dogs can sleep through most things. There will be the advantage of having your hupeeps around more whilst they are on maternity/paternity leave, plus extra visitors to the house who will make a fuss of you, and, if they've been correctly trained, might even bring you a little gift to compensate for the disruption.

As the new arrival grows and develops, they will generally acquire more toys than they know what to do with, which is good for you. There is an obvious similarity between toys for dogs and toys for young children so you can take advantage of the surplus and add to your own stash. The best moment however, is when they start on solid food, particularly when they begin to feed themselves. Their accuracy at finding their mouths is poor in those early days and lots goes on the floor. You will be ready, waiting to help, and with a bit of basic training for the youngster, they will soon be throwing food down especially for you as they will enjoy watching you consume it. Occasionally you'll find your humans take exception to the majority of their carefully prepared baby food feeding the dog and they might try shutting you in another room at meal times. If you have trained your junior correctly however, they will cry piteously when this happens and their parents will quickly come to realise that you are actually an asset at feeding times and should be honoured accordingly.

You will need to be a bit carefully once the youngster is mobile as they are no respecters of personal space and you might find your eyes, ears and tail being poked and grabbed. I once had a friend's junior try and inset a piece of grass up my bottom – we Border Terriers have an erect tail position, what can I tell you, but I dealt with that by trotting along just out of arms' reach. I made sure I positioned myself so that 'Her Indoors' had a clear view of what was going on and, sure enough, she rapidly stepped in and sorted the problem.

You must always be patient with juniors, and if they are getting too much, just remove yourself for a little while. Your family should be trained to provide you with a space where your junior can't go, with judicious provision of stair gates and crates, so that you can have some respite. You need to make sure they are aware of any intrusive behaviours and that they intervene. Make sure you look suitably pained and that you go to them for assistance. I didn't generally have problems with my own juniors, but once when we were caravanning and I was tethered to a stake outside, 'Her Indoors' caught an unsupervised junior from another family poking me with a stick. 'Her Indoors' was robust in my defence, asking the little boy if he would like it if he was similarly treated, and pointing out that he would be upset if I had bitten him in response, and he looked suitably abashed. I was rewarded for my stoicism with lots of fussing and 'Her Indoors' rightly kept a keen eye on me to make sure there was no repeat of this poor behaviour.

Occasionally you will meet a junior who is either unfamiliar with dogs, or has had a poor experience and is scared. It's easier for me in these circumstances because I'm a small dog so children don't find me too threatening, but if you are big, try sitting or lying down. Be very calm and quiet, and if they pluck up the courage to approach, respond gently with licking and tail wagging. It might be a bit of trouble to go to, but you will have the knowledge that you have helped to teach them a lesson that will hopefully stay with them for the rest of their lives.

The addition of a junior to your family therefore, with the correct training in place, should be a benefit rather than a problem and I had years of fun with mine. After all, small children like playing repetitive games, just like dogs, so we're ideally suited. There are just a few significant caveats: beware of dressing up clothes, doll's prams, wheel barrows, sledges and water pistols.

Puppies

It might be that the patter of tiny feet isn't of the human kind, and the acquisition of a little furend, to keep you company can, arguably, be more controversial than a human addition. If you would like a companion to share the domestic duties with you, then, as with most things, it's quite easy to subtly influence your owner into thinking it was their idea in the first place. You just need to be very sociable around other dogs, particularly those of the target breed, and look a bit lonely and lost when you are left on your own at home. If this is insufficient, try demonstrating some symptoms of separation anxiety when you are left. You need to start showing distress as soon as they make preparations to leave and ratchet this up until you are scratching at the door whining, barking or howling as they disappear off. Whilst they are out, indulge in some destructive behaviours, shred, chew, raid the bins, whatever takes your fancy. It might be hard but whatever you do don't settle down and go to sleep. Make sure that you are staring out of the door or window when they return, and greet them ecstatically, as if you were sure that they'd never come back. You'll need to keep this up for a while, depending on the resilience of your owner, but sooner or later they'll Google the symptoms or speak to the Vet, and someone will suggest getting you a little pal. Result!

If however, your family should be rude enough to get a companion for you without consulting you first, you may have got a problem. Whilst you can create a huge fuss, refuse to have anything to do with him or her, or even fight with them, do you really want to be responsible for a young dog ending up in a rescue centre? I would suggest that you make your dissatisfaction known. Sulk, have nothing to do with the new arrival, eat their food, steal their toys and sleep in their bed. Don't let them anywhere near you and demand to be kept away from the newcomer. Your owner will get so anxious that you are not going to accept the new dog that they will try anything to placate you: new toys, treats, extra fuss, it will all come your way. Hold out for as long as you can, then give in gracefully. Make sure that the young upstart knows who is boss right from the start, and ensure they comply with the careful training of your family. You don't want all your good work undermined. You might well find there are advantages in having an extra set of paws to help with the rigours of keeping your family in line, so play it to your advantage.

Bereavement

This is a serious topic and one that I hope you will never have to face. We dogs, next to humans, have a relatively short life span, but, if you have an elderly owner or are very unlucky, you can still lose them. By this I don't mean misplacing them temporarily on a walk, but parting with them permanently. When this happens to dogs, it is often referred to as 'going over the rainbow bridge' but with people there are other delicate euphemisms such as 'kicking the bucket', 'popping their clogs' or 'snuffing it' but basically it means they are gone and they won't be coming back. Whilst it is seemly to miss them and to pine for them, some dogs make the mistake of going a bit overboard on the grieving front. There are stories of loyal pooches guarding the grave of their owner, which is all very touching, but, to be frank, they really need to pull themselves together. The rest of your family will need you to provide unconditional love and affection, as they will be struggling, and you can't do that if you're howling by the graveside. I don't mean to be harsh, but you have your duty to do.

If you have a single owner and you lose them, then clearly you have a problem. There are however, lots of fine charities out there to help, plus you'll have the emotional kudos of being a bereaved dog, so you need to gather yourself, ready to go back to the beginning and chose yourself a new family. If at any time, such as after a particularly spectacular misdemeanour, you are likely to be in serious trouble, just go all misty eyed and gaze into the distance, reminding them that you have suffered in life, and you should be forgiven much quicker. You really need to use every situation that life throws at you, to your advantage.

Redundancy

This is something I have personal experience of as it has happened twice to 'Him Indoors'. Whilst you need to be supportive at difficult times, you also need to safeguard your standard of living. It's all very well them having worthy thoughts about doing things they want to do, but you need to ensure there's enough money coming in to keep you in the manner to which you've become accustomed. After all, we pooches don't come cheap and a good dog, or even a naughty one for that matter, deserves the best of everything.

Often there is a period where the person who has been made redundant will be at home. The best way to deal with this is to keep them busy but at the same time maintain a regular routine. 'Her Indoors' had no problem in finding jobs for 'Him Indoors' and he managed to decorate the lounge before he went back to work. I ensured that 'Him Indoors' also benefitted from spending some extra time with me. Aside from the money, it's the people and loss of status they miss. You can compensate by keeping them company and allowing them to temporarily take over some of your caring tasks, then they can bask in the glow of being known as your 'Mum' or 'Dad'. What greater status can there be than that?

New Home

It is unlikely, through the course of your life time, that one home will be sufficient. I'm not referring here to changing your family, but to acquiring a new, physical abode. You need to ensure that your owner doesn't over-stretch themselves, as they need to have plenty of money to spend on you and your little needs and wants, but if there are deficiencies in where you live now, sometimes that can best be addressed by moving to a new property.

When I first came to live with my family, they had a new build house on an estate. This had certain advantages. The house didn't need much in the way of maintenance, which meant they had more time to spend on me. It also had a reasonable size south facing kitchen with a full-length window for sun-puddling and a utility room which I quickly commandeered for myself. There were also lots of other young families around who had dogs so there were plenty of pals to greet and fun to be had. There was a new primary school just up the road, within walking distance of the house, which gave me a guaranteed walk twice a day.

There were however a few significant disadvantages. Builders of new homes have their eye on the profit margin so they often try and squeeze as many houses as possible onto a given piece of land, which means the gardens are usually a bit meagre. Another linked disadvantage can be the proximity of the neighbours and the fact that barking might upset them. In spite of my best efforts in the training department, 'Them Indoors' often used to send me back into the house for making too much noise, particularly when I was playing lively games with my juniors, and this used to rather spoil the fun.

Eventually, they put the house on the market with a view to moving, but it took a long time to sell. I quite enjoyed greeting the fifty odd people who came to view, but 'Them Indoors' got a bit stressed about having total strangers poking around their house, saying how lovely everything was, and then not buying it. When they finally got a buyer, they were struggling to find another house that met their criteria. When they found our present house it ticked a lot of the boxes, but it was in poor condition and needed a lot of work doing to it. It took a bit of persuading and a certain amount of desperation on their part, but they finally took the plunge, which demonstrated excellent training on my behalf. I love this house for one significant reason: the garden. Not only is it a decent size, if also sides on to a field so we get rabbits, foxes and badgers which gives me plenty to sniff at first thing in the morning. The bunnies have even dug a burrow that comes up in our garden and I spend a lot of time with my nose stuck down the hole or sitting patiently outside waiting for one of the little blighters to show themselves. 'Him Indoors' has tried filling it in, but the rabbits always dig through. Anyway, if I had to vote on which house I'd give this one all four paws.

Once you've approved the selection of the new house, there is removal day to deal with. To be honest, the best way is to stay away. Go to a friend or relative, or if this is not possible, access your holiday care arrangements. They can manage without you for a few days and you need them to sort things out and unpack your bedding, equipment and toys, before you can return.

If you've made the mistake of allowing your family to become too dependent on your company and they can't manage without you, hide in a crate or other safe spot and let them get on with it. People tend to get quite stressed at such times so keep your head low and be a bit tolerant. You can safely reinstate their routine within a week or two.

Empty Nesting
Depending on the stage your family are at when you join them, you may be faced with your family going through the inevitable trauma and upheaval of the juniors leaving home. This can be a difficult time for all so you need to consider both your own role and the evolving training needs of the senior family members.

If the juniors go to university, the leaving home process is drawn out so there should be time for everyone to adapt. There will be a flurry of activity in preparation for the big day, with lots of shopping and subsequent moaning about the bills. When this happened in our family, 'Junior Him' had spent the whole summer warning everyone he probably wouldn't get the grades and he wasn't sure if he wanted to go anyway, then he got the grades but not a place in the halls of residence so it was panic stations trying to get everything sorted. 'Her Indoors' bought lots of cleaning products, as had all the mums of the lads he was sharing his house with, and they remained unused and in pristine condition for the entire time he was a university.

There will usually be some upset around the time that the youngster is taken and left at university. Be prepared for both parents to mope around the house, visiting the empty bedroom and sighing. Try and distract them with a bit of tactical naughtiness, and be a bit needy yourself in the affection department. After all, if they have got a gap in their lives for something to love, what better than a dog to fill it. You will play many roles during a lifetime with your family, but child substitute is quite an easy one. Just be wary of having an owner who is keen on domestic crafts. Having spent many years, knitting, sewing and baking for the juniors, 'Her Indoors' transferred the focus of her skills to me. I, of course, was happy to oblige in the food department, and home-made bandanas are okay too, but, to be frank, the knitted dog coat was a step too far and I had to be firm. I looked suitably pained and tried to roll to get it off. She eventually got the message but it was an anxious time.

The empty nesting process for people isn't just about the juniors physically leaving, it's about them recognising that a big phase of their lives has gone and isn't coming back. Although the juniors keep returning for washing, food and central heating, they don't need their parents on a day-to-day basis any more, which after all, is the desired end-point of bringing up children into useful adults. However, you must allow them a reasonable time to grieve for the end of an era, before reminding them that they've still got you to love and look after.

Sometimes this period can be a challenge, but it can also be an opportunity. Once 'Junior Her' had finished university, 'Her Indoors' decided to pack in her day job and become a freelance writer and creative writing teacher. Although I was generally supportive of her finding a new path, I was a bit concerned about the family income; I need my comforts, what can I tell you. My trust has been repaid however, and she seems to be doing ok, although I have to say, I've taught her everything she knows in the writing department.

I'm quite lucky. So far neither 'Him' or 'Her Indoors' seem to have shown any inclination to trade each other in for a younger model. 'Him Indoors' has resisted the urge to start wearing tight trousers and a comb-over, whilst 'Her Indoors' hasn't dyed her hair purple, had a tattoo or multiple piercings in places where the sun doesn't shine. I think that if you've got the basics right in the early days, then despite the challenges that life can present along the way, you should be able to weather most things safely.

Chapter Eight

Problems

Even with the best brought up people, there can sometimes be issues that arise and you need to know how to address them. As with most things in life, it's better to catch problems early whilst they are still relatively minor, rather than ignoring them and hoping they'll go away, which only serves to allow them to develop into larger issues. There are a range of common problems but don't worry, there are plenty of places to seek help so don't be afraid to ask.

Separation Anxiety

Whilst you obviously don't want to be left on your own frequently for long periods of time, you also want to be able to enjoy a little peace and quiet and some time to ruminate and catch up on your napping. Whilst most owners are okay with this, sometimes they can get very anxious about being parted from you even for short periods of time. Whilst it is tempting to indulge them and allow them to stay at home with you, in reality, this only perpetuates the problem. You don't want to be in a situation where you are being smuggled into places that really aren't suitable for a dog, or even worse, left in a car with all the perils which that entails. It is also not safe for you to wait outside a shop on your own. Years ago, people used to leave babies as well as dogs, outside, but it really isn't a good idea these days. Remember, all dogs, whilst priceless to their family, are also worth hard cash to someone else. If you left hundreds of pounds tied to a lamppost, you wouldn't expect it to be there when you got back. You need to ensure your family see you in the same light and leave someone with you. If there's ever any danger of being left alone, bark, howl, do whatever it takes. Even if your family are a bun short of a picnic, hopefully they will notice the disapproving looks of other people and will quickly return. If all else fails, work on the tether and follow them into the shop. That should sort it!

In order to make them feel more comfortable about leaving you, you need to try and be reasonably well-behaved which is a bit tedious. When you are a puppy, you can get away with a bit of chewing and incontinence, but this is probably not a good idea as an adult dog. Train them to leave you some treats, ideally hidden in a toy so that you can have fun getting them out, and some water. With advanced training you might get them to leave the radio or TV on so that you have something to listen to. Settle down in your bed and have a nice kip, investigate parts of the house or kitchen that you are not normally allowed to explore, and relax. When they come home, greet them warmly but try not to go over the top. Now that I'm a senior, if 'Them Indoors' come home a bit late, or I'm tired, I don't even bother to get up, I just pay suitable homage with a bit of gentle tail wagging and a pleased expression.

Separation anxiety can also influence holiday arrangements. You need to make a considered decision about this one. Sometimes, if it's a dog friendly holiday, it can be good fun to go along too and enjoy a change of scenery and scents. But if it's a holiday that involves tedious hours in the car, particularly if it's abroad where it can be very hot, you might prefer to stay at home. With all your good training, they will obviously be leaving you in capable hands, so you need to reassure them. When I went off to kennels as a younger dog, or now, when I go to my individual carers, I always demonstrate my happiness with the arrangement by trotting off, tail wagging, without a backwards glance. To be honest, 'Her Indoors' struggles a bit with leaving me so it is only fair to make it a bit easier. My carer will often text her when she's away and send a little photo of me, to reassure her, and this can be a useful device to use with the anxious owner.

Occasionally, you might find an owner who has the opposite tendency and thinks it is fine for you to be left on your own regularly without visits or attention for long periods of time whilst they are at work. This is clearly not acceptable and you need to be firm. Bark and annoy the neighbours, chew the fixtures and fittings and use the floor for your toileting arrangements. Harsh, I know, but it needs to be done.

Fears and Phobias
Now I'm a fearless kind of dog, although unfurling carrier bags need treating with the suspicion they rightly deserve, and fireworks, back in the days when I could hear them, needed barking at. People however, are often subject to a range of fears, which if taken to excess, can disrupt everyday life for everyone.

Spiders and snakes are quite common provokers of high levels of fear, as are rats and mice. Now I personally have a simple solution to this issue, I deal with them in true terrier fashion. There is just a word of warning with this. However much your owner may dislike something when it's alive, for some inconceivable reason, they like them even less when they're dead. 'Junior Her' hates spiders but gets quite distraught when I catch them in my mouth, particularly if the legs stick out between my teeth. I don't know why, one big swallow and they're gone. However, if you are not the type of dog who likes to get involved in the regulation of other animals in the household vicinity, don't, just allow them to call in paid professionals to deal with the problem.

Some people are terrified of flying, but as we dogs are not generally allowed on flights unless we're small enough to fit in a hand baggage sized carrier, I would advise not getting involved. It's inherently sizest of airlines not to allow dogs of any description in the cabin; imagine the uproar if they declared that people over a certain height or weight would have to travel in the hold, so leave them to sort it out with special desensitisation flights for those of a nervous disposition. If all else fails they can always take a boat.

Some fears that people have are also shared by their dogs. Thunder storms are a good case in point. One of 'Her Indoors' distant relatives used to be so scared of them that at the first sign, she would hide in the under-the-stairs cupboard. I don't know if she had a dog, but I'm sure that if she did, they'd be happy to hide with her. 'Them Indoors' seem to like them, and usually stand by the window to watch the show. When I was younger, I found it difficult to distinguish between thunder storms and fireworks; they were both noisy with flashes of light, what can I tell you, so I used to bark at both, just to be on the safe side. Some juniors are told tales of thunder being the actions of demons, giants or Gods, but as we dogs know, that is clearly a load of old nonsense, thunder storms are caused by moisture, unstable air and lift, who are they kidding.

Aggression

Whilst people, like dogs, differ in their tolerance to others and to particular situations, you need to be very wary of signs of aggression in your owner.

This can be manifested in a number of ways. Road rage is a common problem which can vary from a minor irritant to a major concern. Most people react negatively to stupid things that other people do on the road, particularly when safety is jeopardised, so it is only fair to allow a bit of horn tooting, blaspheming, and general muttering, under normal circumstances. 'Him Indoors' is usually very patient when driving, but 'Her Indoors' can have a bit of a short fuse. The worst time was when 'Junior Him' was learning how to drive. She got very fed up with other road users intolerance of a learner driver, sitting right on his bumper, overtaking in dangerous locations and tooting when they got impatient. Fortunately I wasn't in the car for any of his practise runs, but on one occasion 'Junior Him' did point out upon their return, that if he had used language like that, he'd have been in trouble. She also found it helpful that the horn was located in the centre of the steering wheel so that she could reach it from the front passenger seat. I'm not sure that she set him a very good example.

Sometimes owners can be aggressive as a response to other people being critical of their dogs and how they look after or train them. Whilst it is natural for owners to be protective of you, it's best to encourage a 'live and let live' approach, after all, everyone is entitled to their opinion, however misguided it might be. Remember the old saying 'sticks and stones may break my bones but names can never hurt me'. Mind you, I prefer to chew on sticks and small stones, swallowing the latter, much to the distress of 'her Indoors' who worries that they'll wedge somewhere. I've been doing it for a life-time and nothing bad has happened to me yet. And I don't mean to tell tales, but some of the language that's used over my misdemeanours would make anyone's ears burn, I can tell you. Even worse these days is that my 'alternative names' are usually prefaced with the word 'old'. Do they think I have no feelings? I prefer the word 'senior', it has a bit more dignity about it. Anyway, your owner will find that once they've acquired a dog, everyone will have an opinion on the best way to treat it, even if they've never owned a dog themselves and, frankly, haven't got a clue. It's a bit like when you first take a new baby out in a pram. Try posting an innocent question on social media, for example, whether or not to crate your dog, and you will get the full spectrum of responses, from the angry 'They're a dog, not a hamster' to those who've happily turned crates into little safe havens, the equivalent of a dog palace. Take your pick! My personal view, for what it's worth, is that provided we dogs and our well-being are the prime focus of any decision, then whatever suits is fine with me. I'm not that picky.

Occasionally owners can be aggressive in the defence of their dog from physical harm, and it's difficult to criticise this provided the reaction is proportionate. We dogs do occasionally have little disagreements, but sometimes these can escalate into something more sinister. If this happens to you, don't be too proud to seek help from your owner, after all they set themselves up as pack leader, and, to quote from the Batman movie, 'With tremendous power comes tremendous responsibility'.

You need to train your owner in how to respond appropriately in these instances as people get injured trying to separate fighting dogs. Get them to make a really loud, sharp noise at close range as that can sometimes work if things haven't escalated too far. Water works well but can be difficult when out on a walk as a bucket is a bit cumbersome. When 'Her Indoors' was having trouble with a rather grumpy Scottish Terrier who kept having a go every time he saw me, she bought a child's water pistol and kept it in her pocket. If the dog started, she used to give it a good squirt. I know it sounds mean, but they need to aim for the face; it's only water, it won't do any harm. The surprise of a cold jet up the hooter usually deters all but the most determined. The only downside of this is that cheap water pistols usually leak. Still, what's a damp patch between friends!

Other tactics that we've seen used include a compressed air canister that makes a rather alarming hissing noise, or a coat thrown over the offending dog's head so that they are suddenly plunged into darkness. 'Her Indoors', as I've already mentioned, once successfully used the technique of suddenly opening a brolly in another dog's face, although this clearly requires them to be suitably equipped from the outset. She's also found that, if the worst comes to the worst, using a foot, protected by a stout walking boot, to separate sparring dogs is a safer option than plunging your hands into a melee of snapping teeth, although it does come with the risk that you might be accused of kicking the offending canine.

The other forms of aggression that are clearly intolerable both legally and morally, are from nasty owners getting dogs to do their dirty work by being aggressive on their behalf, either to people or other animals. They are clearly repugnant human beings and need a serious bite on the bum, although of course, that isn't allowed from us dogs.

Noise

Some people, like dogs, have a natural tendency to be a bit vocal and this is generally not a problem. After all, I'm a terrier, and we always have a lot to say for ourselves. It's not that we bark for no reason, it's just that there's a lot to comment on. For example, when I'm out in the garden, there's birds flying overhead, particularly the large ones like pigeons or crows. 'Him Indoors' can never really understand why I dislike them so much, but they're descended from the dinosaurs, the birds that is, not 'Him Indoors', although saying that…. Then there are cats to rebuke, squirrels who sit there taunting me from the tree tops, twitching their tails provocatively and chattering away. They're lucky I'm just giving them verbal abuse. If only I could fly! We've got rabbits which I bark at in frustration if they escape, and similarly, now my eyesight isn't as sharp as it once was, flies. Then there's the neighbouring dogs. 'Her Indoors' sends me inside if I bark at them too much, but I notice her having a good chat with our neighbours through the hedge so what is the difference? Perhaps, with the value of hindsight, I should have trained them to be a bit more tolerant in the noise department.

Noise problems with people fall into various categories. There are the noises that they make in their every day life activities, such as mechanical noises, and you need to make a clear decision as to which are acceptable and which are not. The washing machine is fine by me, in fact I rather like it as experience has taught me that at the end of the final spin cycle comes a trip down the garden to hang out the washing, at least on dry days. The vacuum cleaner noise however, is not.

I don't know what it is with people, but they often have an odd idea about cleanliness. Just as I've got the kitchen into a suitable state, with a bit of fur blowing round, a fine layer of grit from my coat to give my paws a bit of traction on the otherwise smooth kitchen floor, and odd bits of grass and crumbs of food to sustain me between meals, then along comes the vacuum cleaner and spoils it all. When I was younger, I used to display my displeasure by attacking the cleaner vigorously in the hope that this would deter them, but I have to admit that on this training issue, I've failed. I now take the more pragmatic attitude of looking pained and keeping out of the way until the whole sordid business is over.

I'm also not keen on the lawn mower, although I accept the necessity of it otherwise the grass would be so long I wouldn't be able to get through it. When I was younger, I made the mistake of trying to train them out of cutting it so frequently by looking unhappy and scared, but this back fired rather. I got sent indoors instead. Now I display the same pained face I use with the vacuum cleaner and stick very close to 'Her Indoors'. She gets a bit grumpy with my dog's breath and with my attempts to climb on her lap if the lawn mower comes too close, but I've trained her into displaying a good level of tolerance to both of these things which means that I am generally able to stay in the garden throughout the whole process.

One noise that I have a particular dislike to and that I'm sure most canines would find objectionable, is the smoke alarm. One of ours is in the hall, just outside the kitchen door, and if 'Him Indoors' is cooking certain foods such as burgers or sausages, he inevitably sets it off. It is extremely loud, and even though I'm suffering a bit from senior deafness these days, it causes me actual discomfort. I make my feelings plain by looking pained, a useful expression to master in the noise control department, as soon as the sausages or burgers come out of the packet and the grill is opened. I also go and sit on the mat, right next to the back door, which usually results in them shutting the door between the kitchen and the lobby, reducing the impact of the alarm on my delicate ears. In fairness, my careful training has resulted in them keeping the kitchen door into the hall shut, but occasionally, someone will need to go out to the dining room at a critical moment and set it off. I've also learnt not to take any notice of the reassurance that they give me before they start grilling; they're empty promises, or the apologies they offer to me when they've triggered it; I can't hear them anyway, my ears are still ringing.

In addition to the noises that can't be avoided or are accidental, there are also those they make deliberately and you will need to express a view as to whether or not these are acceptable. 'Them Indoors' like having music on in the house and listening to the radio, which is generally fine with me. They both like Radio Four and tend to have it on over breakfast, and I get an update on the news of the day and can make an informed decision on which politicians I'd allow to stroke me and which ones deserve chasing down the garden path, or worrying, in John Humphries style. 'Him Indoors' likes Classic FM which is okay except for the adverts. I'm not sure what a stair lift is, but as I've yet to successfully train 'Them Indoors' to let me upstairs, I'm not sure it would be any use to me although I suspect I'm in the right age bracket. 'Her Indoors' has a worrying tendency to play the hits of the

80s, given half a chance, so it's just as well she doesn't often get unfettered access to the sound system and that when she does, she really doesn't have a clue how to operate it, bless her!

One thing that is mercifully in the past but which I did strongly object to was when 'Junior Her' learnt to play the violin at primary school. I don't want to be too critical as she was just a little girl, but suffice to say, the violin was nicknamed 'Squeaky! She usually practised upstairs in her bedroom, but occasionally, when she wanted to demonstrate her improvement or seek help for a tricky bit, she used to play it downstairs. Dear Dog! The only option was to howl loudly to try and drown out the sound but this backfired somewhat as 'Junior Her' thought I was singing along. I think 'Her Indoors' understood; she had to go to the lessons after all. I think we all breathed a sigh of relief when that particular phase was over and Squeaky was retired from active service. Having said that, 'Her Indoors' sister, who is very musical, has three daughters, all of which learnt two instruments each through their formative years. Although their family pooch must have suffered, the youngest is now a professional cellist for the Bournemouth Symphony Orchestra, so the sacrifice was not in vain.

Stress
One of the main factors you'll need to guard against in your family is stress. This can be defined as 'the on-going urge to strangle certain people around you against the society imposed requirement to exercise restraint'. In this modern world, a certain amount of stress is unavoidable,

but you can do quite a bit with your training to mitigate this where possible.

Work, and the need to earn sufficient money to keep a roof over your head, food in your dog bowl and pay the Vet's bills, is definitely a stress factor. Some people add to the usual stresses of having a boss and, depending on their role, staff, by working too far away from home with the additional strain of a long commute. In our part of the world, the well documented problems with the railways have caused considerable difficulties with one man stating that he'd given up his job in London as he felt angry all the time. Now us dogs may not be able to solve the problems of the road and rail networks, although there are times when I honestly think we could make a better job of running them, but we can support our owners in mitigating the stress.

It has, for example, long been known that stroking a dog lowers blood pressure. So when we solicit a quick stroke, we are not in fact, being selfish, we are doing our people good, which is something I keep in mind when I've got my eyes shut, enjoying a good tummy tickling. Also, going out for a brisk walk in the fresh air is good for stress, so we can help with that too. If you manage things correctly, you can encourage you owner to work from home at least a few days a week. 'Her Indoors' works from home permanently, and I like to think I played my part in that life-style choice. She can have me keeping her company in her office in the garden, although she does find my tendency to root around, chewing on whatever I find when her attention is diverted, a bit annoying. She also isn't keen on me lying right behind her wheelie chair as she has to remember I am there when she moves. She also doesn't like me snoring loudly as she reckons it affects her concentration but jealousy is rather an un-lovely emotion if you ask me. Anyway, I generally prefer the comfort of my own bed during the day, so she calls in to see me every hour or so when she makes a cup of tea or nips to the loo. I also take her for regular little walks around the garden which I know she finds de-stressing, unless there are any rabbits or grass snakes around.

Some dogs actually influence their owners' occupations directly. For instance, where would 'Her Indoors' be in her writing without my good example? There are also people whose crafting businesses are entirely based around their dogs, or whose endeavours were inspired by their pooches. My favourite dog food was, in fact, a result of the particular dietary requirements of a Border Terrier. And take my worth illustrator, Sally C Greenfield. She is an artist, specialising in dogs and horses. She is also a Border Terrier breeder and owns two herself, Boadicea and Mayhem, who sound like worthy furs although I've not met them to date. So, if you are really serious about de-stressing your owners' occupations you can guide them in a whole new direction, often to your mutual benefit.

Over-indulgence
Sometimes people who are subject to stress, can resort to over-indulgence, and, in serious cases, if left untreated, addiction. Now we've already covered alcohol briefly, but if setting a good example in the units department isn't sufficient, you might have to take a more active role. Try taking a slurp from their drink yourself. As well as being quite pleasurable, it also tends to put them off drinking

the rest of the glass, I can't think why. Then you can knock their bottle over. Even with the quickest reflexes some of it will have been spilt. I've also seen some good examples of responsible furs, on social media, using their paws to knock hands away from glasses. That should get the message across.

Smoking is often seen as a tricky one but I've got a solution for that. I pinch the cigarettes directly out of the fingers of the smoker. 'Her Indoors' thinks it's because I mistake them for something edible, but that just goes to show how much she underestimates me. I know that they are doing themselves harm so I'm just saving them from themselves. Maybe I should be available on prescription.

You can also try upping the spending they are having to make on you. Try developing some ambiguous medical condition that requires lots of visits to specialist vets, a specific and pricey diet and lots of tablets, ointments and hydrotherapy. By the time they've paid for all this, they won't have any money left for cigarettes, and once they've given up you can gradually get better so that you can spend your time and money on more enjoyable things.

Over-eating is another increasing problem. You need to ensure that they get out there and burn the calories so encourage them to take two lengthy walks with you every day. Another really good ploy if you are a small to medium weight dog is to refuse to get on the scales at the Vets. It might take a while, but sooner or later someone will suggest your owner picks you up and stands on the scales with you, then they deduct their weight from the total, in order to get yours. In our surgery, the scales are in the waiting room, or should it perhaps be the weighting room, so the public humiliation would probably be a very effective incentive. Us dogs can be very inventive in the interests of our humans.

Mental Health Issues
Mental health has recently been in the news with an estimated one in three people suffering from a mental health issue, so if your human is affected, don't be afraid to seek help as promptly as you would for a physical health need. Remember, it is not your fault and it's nothing to be ashamed of.

We dogs can help our humans with a whole range of mental health issues; depression, anxiety and loneliness. We are also great for low self-esteem. After all, we can provide the kind of unconditional love that all people need. We don't care what they look like or how much money they've got and we're always pleased to see them. We're a force for good in their lives and with our support, most problems can be alleviated or overcome entirely.

So, if life with your owner doesn't always run on rails, don't be despondent, there are lots of things you can do to get things back on track, particularly if you act quickly. Whilst we may not have a magic wand we can wave, we certainly do have tails we can wag, and that can solve a lot of things. Don't let the thought of potential problems put you off. You have got a whole lifetime with your owner so it's worth weathering a few tough patches and behavioural issues so that you can enjoy the good times together.

Chapter Nine

Aging

Whatever age your owners are when you acquire them, you can guarantee one thing: they'll only get older. I've seen 'Them Indoors' transition from being in their thirties, with young children, to being in their fifties with grown up children, and, particularly in the case of 'Him Indoors' who is six years older, heading towards retirement.

Mid-life Crisis
Aging isn't necessarily a problem, but you do have to watch out for that mid-life bit. There comes a point when they realise that they've probably got more of their lives behind them than in front, and that some of the things they wanted to do when they were young: win a grand prix, score a goal for England, fit into a size eight dress,

run ten marathons in ten days and travel to the moon, are not realistically going to happen. Sometimes, this realisation that life is short, can make them frantically try and recreate their youth with trips to festivals, age-inappropriate clothing and/or hair pieces, dodgy relationships with younger versions of their current spouse, and plastic surgery. Some of these things, like hair-pieces can be challenged head-on, if you'll excuse the pun, and, as a terrier, I know exactly what treatment I'd give a 'rug' if I met one. Some of it however, you just have to weather and hope that it's a passing phase.

I've been quite lucky as far as 'Them Indoors' are concerned. 'Him Indoors' sometimes plays his Bruce Springsteen tracks quite loudly, but I don't object to a bit of rock myself. 'Her Indoors' has basically been middle-aged all her life, with her love of knitting, home crafts and gardening, so has finally found her comfort zone and is relishing it. She may have a slightly worrying penchant for age-inappropriate cars but what's a Mini convertible rather than a sensible hatchback between friends? And they're not too embarrassing in the clothing department either. 'Him Indoors' has always had a tendency to dress like a middle-aged man so his wearing of slippers, fleeces and trousers with comfy waistbands is now officially sanctioned rather than subversive and there's thankfully no signs of over-tight leather jeans, shirts unbuttoned to the waist and visible chest hair ornamented with chunky jewellery.

'Her Indoors' is usually fairly conservative in her dress, although there was a slightly worrying phase, when 'Junior Her' was a teenager, and she tried to actively encourage her mum to dress a bit younger. This was generally resisted by 'Her Indoors', but once, when she went clothes shopping with 'Junior Her' she did give in and tried on a skirt that was considerably shorter than those she normally wears. Once she had wriggled into it, she rather thought it proved the point so she ventured to show 'Junior Her' who was momentarily taken aback. Rallying herself, she ventured the opinion that "All the men will love you in that", which, as 'Her Indoors' crisply pointed out, wasn't actually the look that she was trying to achieve, at her age.

Teenage Years

If you've joined a family with younger children, be warned, they don't stay like that for ever. The cute little girl in pig tails, with freckles who wants to give you rides in her doll's pram and tie bows in your fur, will soon be experimenting with make-up and moaning about boys. And the young lad, who wants you to stand in as a dinosaur or dragon, or join him in his 'den' made out of a couple of sheets held in place with a broom handle, will soon be smelling so strongly of deodorant and hair-gel that you'll wish your nose was several notches less sensitive. Try sneezing loudly and repeatedly every time they come near you and see if they take the hint.

Your role in all of this however, is relatively simple. Keep your head down, don't tell tales and leave their parents to deal with the angsty bits. You can always partake in any new bad habits, make friends with even the most unpromising and unprepossessing of the other youngsters they bring to the house and you will be there to drink any surplus beer, eat mouldy food left festering on the floor, sniff ripe laundry and offer a furry shoulder for them to cry on when their teenage love life is thwarted. They will need you as much as ever.

The Senior Years
It might be that if your owners were already more mature when you joined them, that you oversee the transition into their seniority. Again, this can have advantages for you, as they will be less preoccupied with work and family matters as they grow older, and have more time and affection to lavish on you. Hopefully they will have made sufficient provision for their old age when they were younger, so you'll be able to benefit from a comfortable standard of living too.

Sometimes life-long dog owners get reluctant to take on a new dog as they get older, worrying about what will happen to their pet should the worst happen to them. They also get concerned about the demands of exercising a young dog and whether they'll have the energy to keep up. This strikes me however as an area for re-education. There are charities out there that specialise in re-homing older dogs, which people often avoid when looking for a new pet. What could be a happier match? If you're a senior yourself and you are looking for a new home, go for the oldies, they'd be ideal. You can sit in front of the fire, chomping biscuits with your remaining sound teeth, not hearing each other however loud the vocals and shaking your head disapprovingly at the antics of youngsters together, whilst both enjoying Countryfile on TV. Nothing could be more fitting.

Common Ailments

One of the factors that you'll need to take into account with the older owner, is the fact that they are more prone to suffering from the variety of ailments that often accompany old age. Some of the more common ones are outlined below:

- Deafness – No problem! They won't be able to hear you bark quite so much so there will be less complaining about noise.

- Failing eye-sight – Great! They won't notice your dog hair and muddy paw prints on the floor.

- Moving a bit more slowly – This can be annoying if you're a young pup full of energy, but then it is unlikely that anyone would be fast enough for you. If you are more senior and like to linger over a sniff, then they will probably move at the perfect speed for you anyway.

- Poor memory – Another one that can be an advantage. They are less likely to remember your misdemeanours and more likely to give you a second meal by mistake.

- Arthritis – This can affect the hands and fingers which might, mercifully, slow them up in the knitting department. If it's the hips, it can hinder their mobility which might become an issue if it affects your walks, but don't be disheartened, there is lots that can be done with plastic these days and they'll soon be back up to speed.

- Digestive disorders – It might be that as they get older, certain foods that they used to happily eat, may now upset their digestion. Not a problem:

they'll have you at hand to eat up any surplus food, for their own good, naturally.

- Dental problems – These days it is common for people, like dogs, to hang onto their teeth for a lifetime, but again, they might find that certain foods are more difficult to deal with. That's where you come in, providing a solution for hard crusts and crisp apples, they don't even have to ask.

- Mobility issues – Sometimes very elderly people or those with specific illnesses or conditions, might find that they are not as mobile as they use to be. This doesn't have to be a problem. I've seen dogs being happily 'walked' by people in mobility scooters and these provide the advantage that, should you get a bit weary yourself, you can hop on board. I've even seen small dogs riding quite happily in a basket on a scooter, until they get to a stretch of grass where they hop out for a bit of exercise and to do their ablutions, then they jump back in for the ride home – perfect!

Sheltered Accommodation and Nursing Homes

Sometimes it can get to the stage where people struggle to cope in their existing homes and have to 'downsize' to something easier to manage or where someone can keep a general eye or look after them. It used to be that moving into sheltered accommodation or a nursing home signalled the end of the relationship with their dog, and many put off making this much-needed step for precisely that reason. However, as the years go by, more and more places are recognising the benefit of people having their beloved pets with them and allow them to join them in these different living environments. This is also a great arrangement for dogs as, in addition to your doting owner, you'll be surrounded by other people of senior years who might well enjoy patting and stroking an amiable pooch. Tummy tickles all round then!

The Aging Dog

As our life span is relatively short compared to a person, although amazingly long if you compare it to a hamster, which just goes to prove that everything in life is relative, we dogs tend to age quite quickly. There is some variation, according to breed, with the giants of the canine world such as Irish Wolfhounds and Great Danes, struggling to make it into double figures, whilst terriers, thankfully for me, often enjoy reaching the ripe old age of fifteen and beyond. I'm presently fourteen, and whilst it would be true to say that I can't do quite as much as I used to, I'm still in pretty good fettle. Provided I keep away from rainbow bridges and avoid moving towards the light, I should hopefully be good for a few more years yet. After all, I feel like I owe it to 'Him Indoors' to live as long as possible.

However, dogs, like people, do have some particular needs as they get older, which can be summarised as follows:

- Comfort – the older we get, the more we need our creature comforts. It used to be that I could sleep on any surface, and happily walk in any weather, whereas now, like the princess and the pea, I need a good thick mattress in my dog bed and an 'all-weather' coat to keep the worst of the elements at bay. I also reserve the right not to go out at all if the weather is particularly inclement.

- Food – Lots please! There was a time when the Vet recommended giving me senior dog food as apparently it's not as rich as that for younger furs. The net result was that I was hungry all the time and kept sourcing my own food which wasn't always suitable and made me ill. 'Her Indoors' is not slow to respond to that sort of training, and put me back onto regular dog food which was a relief. There is a school of thought that as we senior dogs are not so physically active, we should eat less, but I don't subscribe to this theory either. What we may lack in physical activity we make up for in mental exercise. It might look like we're snoozing all day but actually we're in deep thought and that takes a lot of energy. 'Her Indoors' lets me get away with that line of reasoning provided I don't get too comfortable around the middle. She worries about the effect of any excess weight on my arthritis so she keeps a careful eye on my diet. I keep a similarly careful eye on the level of food in my bowl so it's a constant battle of wills.

- Exercise – Older dogs don't need as much exercise as younger dogs. I had to put my paw down firmly about this as 'Them Indoors' were still expecting me to do a long walk with them every weekend. I made my feelings clear by sitting down and refusing to move. Now they sometimes take me for a short snooter over the playing fields, then drop me at home and do the rest of the walk themselves. It just shows what good training can achieve. However, I do still go for a walk every day. Just because I'm a senior, doesn't mean that I don't like to get out and about, having a slow read of the pee-mail and meeting up with my friends. I also enjoy the odd longer walk when I meet up with other Border Terrier pals, and 'Her Indoors' is always surprised at how far I walk on these occasions, bearing in mind the restrictions I impose at home. Of course, she's forgetting my guiding principle: the 'what's in it for me' rule. If I'm at an exciting gathering of all my pals, I forget that I'm a senior and keep up with the youngsters. When it's just boring old 'Them Indoors' there just isn't the same incentive.

Some dogs have trained their people into providing them with senior transport, in the form of buggies, for when they get tired. I haven't got one of those, although I can quite see the advantages, but I have got a special back pack for carrying small to medium sized dogs in. On one occasion, when I was attending a Border Terrier Tweet-up that turned out to be a much longer route than originally anticipated, I got very tired and 'Her Indoors' had to carry me. Although she had some help, she moaned quite a bit about me being heavy – what a wimp – why does she think she has gym membership? - but after that she bought a doggy back pack for me to ride in. Having tried it out recently, at another Border

Terrier get together, I can thoroughly recommend it. It's comfy and 'Her indoors' couldn't see when people were sneaking me treats.

- Ailments – Dogs, like people, suffer from a range of ailments as they get older, and some need specific owner training in order for you to get the appropriate support.

Arthritis – This can be helped by taking suitable medication and I've done some legal drug experimentation in order to find the one that is most effective for me. My preferred Vet at our local practise, who's not exactly in the first flush of youth himself, admitted to 'Her Indoors' that he'd tried it and that it was good stuff! I'm sure there are rules about that somewhere but it's good to know that he's not above taking his own advice. Anyway, you need to make sure that you have comfortable bedding, wear a harness rather than a collar to prevent undue strain, and exercise in moderation – sorted!

Deafness – It's important to distinguish here between the kind of selective deafness that all dogs, regardless of age, suffer from, usually when hearing a command that contains the words 'drop', 'no' or 'come', and the more serious kind that actually prevents you hearing things to your advantage like the treats tin being opened. It can also be responsible for some serious communication issues between you and your family.

When I'm outdoors, I can't hear where 'Her Indoors' is and her calling me, so we spend happy times wandering round the garden trying to find each other. She got fed up with this, and forever resourceful, bought a falconry bell which she attaches to my collar. Amazon have a lot to answer for. Apart from the undignified similarity to a cat, she can now tell exactly where I am by tracking me down by sound. She has a horrible habit of sneaking up behind me, when I'm quietly going about my business, and prodding me on the bottom. She seems to find it amusing when she makes me jump, and although I'm a tolerant sort of dog, this kind of behaviour clearly isn't acceptable. Apart from the obvious lack of manners, she has caught me red-pawed on a few occasions, doing things that might, strictly speaking, have been on the banned list, which isn't good. It's a training issue I'm working on. I've done my best to dislodge the bell but without success so far. I've also tried to help her loose it but, unfortunately, she keeps it on the key rack out of my reach. As I'm not a dog to give up easily, I'm sure I'll find a solution, it's just a matter of time and persistence as it usually is with training.

Something I've had more success with is in getting 'Her Indoors' to use hand signals as a form of communication. It's hardly British Sign Language compliant, but she uses a sweeping arm gesture to signal me to come, with a pointy finger to indicate the preferred direction of travel. She also uses a thumbs-up to indicate I've been good and a sternly wagging finger on the rare occasion that I might have accidentally infringed some petty regulation that she has imposed on my behaviour. 'Sit' is indicated by a gently poke at my rear end, and 'lie down' by patting the floor with her flat hand. As this was the hand signal that, in my youth, was used to get me to drop my ball, there was a bit of confusion to begin with, but she got the hang of things eventually, you just have to be patient.

One of the advantages with hand signals is that they are easily ignored if the demands are not timely or are unreasonable. All you have to do is studiously refuse to look in your owner's direction and you cannot be accused of disobedience. It would take a very hard-hearted person to get cross with a deaf dog for not listening. I do however, confess to making a bit of a mistake in my training. When I'm waiting for something that is obviously in my favour, for example, for her to stop gardening and go inside to make my tea, I watch her body language with an almost obsessive focus. She has discovered that I can read signs so subtle, that I know when she's finally heading inside, before she does. This has undermined my refusal to notice obvious, sweeping gestures at other times and has led to some unseemly name calling. Still, I think, in general terms, I can claim a modest success, and that this is one barrier we have successfully overcome.

There are, of course, some other advantages to being deaf. Fireworks, which used to disturb me greatly, don't bother me at all. Also, I don't hear other dogs barking at me, the door bell ringing or the bin men collecting the bins which means that I am saved the effort of barking at all of them in return. I can happily lie in my basked, snoozing away, lost in deep, doggy contemplation.

Dental and dietary issues – It would be fair to say that my teeth are not as gleaming white as they used to be and that some of them have lost their pointy ends in various mishaps over the years. I don't know who halitosis is, but he doesn't seem very popular as I hear his name mentioned a lot in derogatory terms when I'm breathing heavily. I had a gum infection and the Vet did gently suggest that a bit of dental work might not go amiss but I wasn't keen as it would mean me having a general anaesthetic. The last time I had one of those, I woke up without two small, but important parts of my anatomy, so I'm not sure I'd trust them not to remove something else whilst they were about it. Instead, I've gone down the homeopathic route and have a supplement of seaweed extract that 'Her Indoors' adds on a daily basis to my food. I've also continued to have my daily dental chew and I haven't had any problems since. They also taste nice so the regime gets a paws up from me.

Whilst I've continued to have an 'all grist to the mill' policy when it comes to edibles, and quite frankly, the not quite edibles, I do find that my stomach is a little less cast iron than it used to be and it takes less these days before 'Her Indoors' has to resort to a floor cloth and bucket. She tends to moan about his but I can't see why. Housework has been proven to use up quite a few calories, something 'Him Indoors', probably advisedly, hasn't yet mentioned, so she should be grateful. She needs all the exercise she can get at her age.

It also takes a bit longer to get rid of a bug once I've got it, but I've trained 'Her Indoors' well in the suitable provision of invalid food. If I'm very poorly, it's just white boiled rice. She adds a stock cube to the water in an effort to make it marginally less boring, but it only helps a little, if I'm honest, and the rice still gets stuck around my teeth. When I'm just a bit off colour, she adds plain cooked chicken or a little bit of tinned tuna to the rice, which is a vast improvement. She did read somewhere, that scrambled egg is good for dogs with upset tummies, so she made me some. What's that all about - little bits of tasteless, rubbery egg. I took one nibble, as a gesture towards her effort, but refused to eat any more just in case she didn't take the hint and made it again. Anyway, whatever your food of choice, you are in a good position to demand it. There's nothing like a worried owner, and you sitting gazing dolefully at your bowl, to get them to whip up some homemade, delicious culinary delight. There have got to be some advantages to being ill.

At the End of the Day
People find death a difficult matter to confront and I think they feel that if they don't discuss it, somehow it isn't going to happen to them or anyone that they love. The uncomfortable fact remains however, that all living things will eventually stop living, and you need to help your owner comes to terms with this. I've done my best, over the years, to gently introduce them to the concept, by delivering an untimely demise on various little furry and feathered creatures, but I can't say that my efforts have been greatly appreciated. Only the other day, I asked to go outside before 'Her Indoors' had eaten her breakfast and was still in a pre-civilised state, and I caught her a baby rabbit, which is no mean feat at my age. Was she grateful? No, she was not. She got cross with me when I

refused to give the little corpse up, and didn't seem to be getting the intended message about the fragility of life and the proximity of death, she just wanted to eat her bran flakes and drink her coffee.

A difficulty sometimes occurs when a dog is ready to go over the rainbow bridge. If nature takes its course, or there is an obvious illness and suffering, then the decision is already taken or is at least clear cut. Sometimes however, there is a just a gradual accumulation of aged infirmities and illnesses, that erode a dog's quality of life, until there is no pleasure left. Some owners find it very difficult to acknowledge that point, and make arrangements for their loyal companion to be helped on their way and, as usual, it is up to the dog to put their paw down and make it clear that they are miserable. Whilst some people shy away from the idea of people being able to make the decision that enough is enough for themselves, although I can't see why myself, they are still allowed to make it for their dogs. I know it is tough, but it demonstrates the ultimate in good training, if they are able to put your needs before their own, and do the right thing by you. Obviously, I haven't been in that situation yet, but I like to feel that if and when the time comes, 'Her Indoors' can be relied upon to behave responsibly. I'm sure 'Him Indoors' will be able to find it in his heart to let me go slightly more easily than 'Her Indoors', although he should beware the return of the puppy stage that might well follow, and I bet he'll miss me more than he thinks.

Chapter Ten

Having Fun

In writing a training manual, I have, necessarily had to focus on some of the sterner issues; the 'does' and the 'don'ts' of human and canine relationships. There is however, a lot of fun that you can have together and you need to train your humans properly in order to maximise that enjoyment.

Birthdays – If you have a well-trained owner, your birthday will attract the kind of celebrations normally associated with royalty. There will be presents, cards, a special meal and, if you're lucky, your very own cake. The twenty-one gun salute and fly-past by the Red Arrows might be missing, but pictures of your own event will grace social media and will take pride of place in family albums, whether real or virtual.

If however, you have failed to make your owner put your needs first in everything, you might well be in the same position as the occasional dog I have met whose family don't even know on which date their birthday falls. If you are a rescue dog, your nearest and dearest might be excused from not knowing the exact day, but they should still have an event to mark the passing of another year – there really is no excuse.

As with all training, it's important to use positive reinforcement, so if they've made an effort to celebrate your birthday, join in with great enthusiasm, as a reward. Over the years, I've perfected the art of unwrapping presents and I now set about any parcel, regardless of intended recipient, with great enthusiasm. After all, it might be for me and I'm not going to take any chances. The preferred technique is to shred the wrapping paper with gusto, making as much mess as possible. Don't worry about the clearing up; you have well-trained staff to take care of that for you. You need to be a bit careful not to similarly shred the present inside, but 'Them Indoors' usually give me a timely reminder if the contents appear in danger.

If the present is something practical but boring such as a new coat or collar, sniff it quickly, just to make sure it's not a toy or some edibles in disguise, and then ignore it completely. That'll teach them for trying to pass off the purchase of something you needed anyway as a present. Do they think we're stupid! If it's something edible, make sure you alleviate that condition, as quickly as possible. People have some strange notions about 'not eating it all at once' or even worse 'saving it until later'. What's that all about? Just get in there quick, before they've had time to draw breath, and start munching.

If the present is a toy, approach it like a dog who's never had a thing to play with in their entire life. Play with it, chew it, store and guard it jealously in your bed. Make sure they realise that toys are a very welcome gift and hopefully they'll repeat the behaviour in the future. After all, think of the pleasure you are giving them, watching you enjoying their efforts. Precisely how you deal with toys will depend a bit on your breed type and natural disposition. Being a terrier, soft rubber or fabric toys have about a five-minute life span before they are disembowelled, de-fluffed and shredded. It's intensely enjoyable during the process, and I always give it my serious concentration until it's suitably disposed of. When it's in bits, 'Her Indoors' puts it in the bin as she worries about me swallowing the dismembered parts, so I sit next to the bin and look sad, so that come the next celebration, the whole glorious process is repeated.

The only soft toy that has ever survived this process is in the shape of a gingerbread man, and he remains untouched and pristine. Every year, the Twitter group that I belong to, the BT Posse, does a secret Santa, and this was part of a rather generous gift that I received. 'Her Indoors', with a touching sentimentality, thinks this is the reason the present remains unscathed. I don't want to shatter her illusions regarding my finer feelings, but he makes rather a comfortable pillow, anyway, he's here to stay. 'Her Indoors' has christened him 'Ginge' which shows a worrying lack of imagination for someone who considers herself a writer, but there's only so much you can teach a person – they've either got it or they haven't.

In my younger days, I used to enjoy a good squeaky toy. Depending on the pitch, the noise is quite intense to us with sensitive hearing, so I had to yowl to accompany the squeaking. For some strange reason, 'Them Indoors' didn't appreciate this and a lot of my squeaky toys used to mysteriously disappear. These days however, with my senior deafness, I don't hear them anyway which makes them rather superfluous to requirements.

The other toy that I always relish but that 'Them Indoors' see as a mixed blessing, is a Frisbee. They enjoy watching me play with it. I stand on the little rim at the edge to get it in a vertical position for a chew, I bounce around the garden flapping it up and down like an over-large tongue, and I shake it back and forwards with a scythe-like action which also has the useful side-effect of deadheading the plants, whether they need it or not. 'Her Indoors' doesn't seem to appreciate this help, which I consider singularly ungrateful, and the family also don't like my technique for getting them to play with me. This involves taking the edge of the Frisbee and jamming the other side of it into their legs, preferably the back of the knees. It sometimes works, but as a training technique it's a bit of a double-edged sword, if you'll excuse the pun, as if it gets a bit much, they confiscate it temporarily. This usually involves putting it on top of one of the water butts in the garden which is particularly unfair as I'm a small dog with short legs. Whilst in my younger days, I'd have tried leaping for it, these days there's not much I can do, and, what's worse, they often forget where they've put it and it languishes there for weeks. The only benefit to this sorry saga is that when they do eventually notice and give it back, I'm always ecstatically pleased to see it, although this can lead to a Groundhog Day style repeat of the whole process.

Whilst all dogs have their own preferences, and you need to train your owners to respect yours, my particular favourite toys are balls of all shapes and sizes. Tennis balls are great fun as they offer the additional entertainment of de-fluffing. There are lots of photos of me proudly holding a naked tennis ball with a pile of suitably coloured fluff next to me and tastefully incorporated into my beard. Once they are shorn of their covering, I then chew them relentlessly until they split, and then it's usually only a short period of time until they're in pieces and relegated to the bin. Still, I get hours of entertainment along the way. Generally, the only balls that survive are the solid rubber kind, and when I was younger I used to pester inexhaustibly, for someone to throw them for me. The technique for training your family involves approaching them with said ball, sitting down nicely – I'm a polite fur, what can I tell you - and dropping the ball pointedly at their feet. If this fails to achieve the desired effect, try dropping it, rather forcibly if necessary, *on* their feet. They might complain a little but they'll be keen to avoid a repeat performance and should actually throw it for you. You'll then need to reinforce this training ad nauseam for the rest of the day, and repeatedly on subsequent days.

People sometimes have a lamentably short attention span when it comes to playing games, so occasionally they will rudely ignore your polite requests.

You need to be firm about this. I've had to drop my ball in the watering can, in planting holes made for new shrubs, on laps, and even on one occasion, in a frothy bucket of window cleaning water. This backfired slightly in that 'Her Indoors' refused to retrieve it for me and eventually, in spite of repeated requests, I had to brave the water and plunge my head in to get it back. I came out decorated in foam looking like Father Christmas, and 'Her Indoors' seemed to find this most amusing. This just goes to show that even with the best training, your owners can still have the occasional lapse from the high standards you set for them.

The best balls are actually those stolen from others. As I've got neighbouring dogs, and there used to be a canine living in our house before we bought it, I occasionally find a ball that isn't, strictly speaking, mine. As 'Her Indoors' cannot work out where it came from, it cannot be easily returned, so, according to the dogs' rules of possession, it immediately passes into my assorted collection where, like a rescued Heinz variety mongrel, is all the more valued for its doubtful origins. A ball is a ball, after all, and what can be nicer than a freebie.

There are, however, a few tricky areas with toys apart from the fact that most only have a very limited life span. One such instance is when they get lost. We dogs have far better senses than people, so trying to persuade your owners that your beloved toy is under the sofa or worse, a prickly bush in the garden, if they can't immediately see it themselves, can be a tedious and frustrating business. We used to have an old shed in the garden which was rather unsatisfactorily raised on brick piers as the ground wasn't level. Anyway, unsurprisingly, I often used to lose balls under there and trying to get 'Her Indoors' to do something about it in a timely fashion was difficult. It meant that she had to get an old broom or other suitable long stick, kneel or lie down on the grass so that she could see where the ball was, and then try and knock it out. Sometimes, depending on the time of year and the weather, she had to get a torch too. This made her, at best a bit slow, and at worst, if she was all dressed up for work, very reluctant to help, so I had to use a rather direct training technique. If she didn't respond to my clear command of sitting there whimpering and staring pointedly under the shed, or running up and down along its length whining, I used to just crawl under the shed myself. It was a bit of a tight squeeze and 'Her Indoors' used to get very anxious about me getting stuck, or even worse, one of the wobbly pillars giving way and the shed squashing me. This used to give a bit more urgency to her efforts to help retrieve the ball. The whole matter was eventually suitably resolved by replacing the shed on a level, solid concrete base. I do miss the fact that the bunnies used to hide under it, which gave me hours of viewing pleasure, but then you can't have everything in this life and, occasionally, compromise is needed for the greater good.

Christmas and other significant holidays – The important thing to remember, when training your humans, is that whilst these events might have important religious, family or secular significance, you should remain a primary focus. 'Her Indoors' starts getting distracted towards the end of November, and by a couple of weeks into December, is usually getting a bit frantic. 'Him

Indoors' retreats to his study and just mutters darkly about Christmas being about family and not about presents, which is code for 'beware the January credit card bills', and I tend to adopt my own unique approach. I'm quite tolerant of the preparations as they usually yield opportunities for the alert canine. There is a flurry of home baking which, in our household at least, results in plenty of dropped food. Some of these can be quite exotic and I'm not sure I would have got to try pistachio nuts under other circumstances.

'Her Indoors' takes the Damsons from the garden at the end of the summer, puts them in a large glass jar, and steeps them in cheap gin until Christmas. She then decants the Damson Gin into nice containers and gives them, with a bottle of good tonic, to her friends as little gifts. This process, does of course, involve removing the damsons from the gin, and the odd one usually gets dropped. I'm there like a shot and before you can say 'one glass or two' I've munched them up and am enjoying the subsequent warm glow. As this is an annual event, I'm there, at the first opening of the jar, awaiting my moment. You need to develop a long memory for seasonal rituals like these.

I've trained my family, particularly 'Junior Her', well in the inclusivity aspects of Christmas, and over recent years, she's hung a Christmas stocking up for me too. This is only right and proper. If I'm going to tolerate some old boy with a beard entering our house in a rather unorthodox fashion in the middle of the night, it's only fair that he should leave a few gifts for the canine home guard too. And I don't want to give the game away should any young people inadvertently get hold of a copy of this book, but it's not always Rudolph who gets the carrot. It's probably a good thing so many dogs enjoy this particular vegetable otherwise the reindeer wouldn't get off the roof after the first street. I'm such a generous fur that I'm happy to help out in the mince pie and sherry department too, he doesn't even need to ask. Anyway, one year 'Junior Her' made the mistake of leaving my stocking in the kitchen, and 'Her Indoors' was awoken in the middle of the night to some strange sounds and found me busy trying to access my presents a little ahead of schedule. In subsequent years my stocking has been placed outside in the hall, which has spoiled that particular activity. There was also some disharmony one year when I actually got more Christmas presents than 'Her Indoors'. I hadn't noted her as the jealous type which just goes to show that you never truly know a person however well you train them, and you need to remember that, after all, they're only human.

Sometimes particular occasions have traditions from which we dogs are unfortunately excluded. This tends to occur with anything that involves chocolate as, in one of life's true injustices, this is poisonous to dogs. 'Junior Her' has always been very sensitive to my needs and she succeeded once in getting me my very own advent calendar with a dog biscuit behind each door. I didn't really see the point in rationing myself to one biscuit per day, and, like 'Junior Him' with his chocolate one, tried to open all the doors in one go. 'Her Indoors' was equally disapproving of both of us and I didn't get an advent calendar the following year which was rather unforgiving of her. She never approved of the chocolate ones for the 'Juniors' anyway as she saw them as embodying the type of materialism that she moans about when the shops start stocking Christmas goodies before Halloween. She thought they should be happy with just a picture behind each door, but I know 'Junior Him' views this as a serious deprivation and unwarranted subversion of his childhood experience.

'Junior Her' also helped one year, in ensuring that I got my very own Easter egg made out of special doggy chocolate. I don't know how she persuaded 'Her Indoors' but she did, and the result was an impressive boxed and foil wrapped egg, just like the conventional ones. I discovered that removing foil involves a very similar technique to removing wrapping paper, and I was in there like a shot. The egg was delicious, and I feel, a just reward for all those careful years of training 'Junior Her'. It's always very pleasing when your particular efforts with the youngsters pay off.

Games – In order to build the bond between you and your family, it's important to play games with them. You'll tend to find that different members of the family incline to different kinds of game so you need to adapt your training style accordingly.

'Her Indoors' is quite good at games that involve tugging. I usually have a special kind of toy that has one end for me to hold and one end for her, which minimises the possibility of any confusion and the potential for minor mishaps should we both try to hold the same end at the same time. It's not my fault that I've only got teeth to hold on with and that human skin is so easily damaged. Anyway, it's a game I like to devote some energy too and I tug my end spasmodically, theatrically growling, rolling my eyes and shaking the toy. On a good day, I can get 'Her Indoors' to respond in kind, which is always quite amusing. She's no idea what she's saying when she's growling, and some of that language definitely didn't come from me, but at least she's entering into the spirit of things.

Sometimes, when I was younger with stronger teeth than I've got now, I used to demonstrate my terrier tenacity in the holding on department, and I'd allow 'Her Indoors' to pick me up off the floor, gripping onto my end of the tugging toy, with just my teeth. We both used to find this quite impressive. Occasionally, when she gets bored of playing in the normal fashion, she's tried hooking her end of the toy round her foot and standing on it so that her level of participation is minimal. I don't put up with any of that nonsense. I stop playing and give her a look, somewhere between accusing and hurt, and that usually promotes a guilty return to proper playing.

Just a word of advice when playing this particular game, particularly if you are a big dog. You need to match the force of your tugging to the size of the person playing with you, particularly if they're juniors. You don't want to end up pulling them off their feet. 'Her Indoors' always attaches a sentimental belief to me being gentle when playing this game with Juniors, but I've learnt that if you want the game to last as long as possible, you don't want any grazed knees, so it is in everyone's interests to be careful.

Some dogs really enjoy playing with bubbles, although this can be a difficult game to initiate in the first instance. You really need some young Juniors around who are bought them as a distraction on a summer afternoon and then you can demonstrate your own liking by chasing them, jumping after them and popping them with your teeth. Very satisfying. Although Juniors have a range of outdoor toys that can be good fun for dogs too, beware of anything that's inflatable. If you accidentally burst their favourite football or inflatable toy, they can be surprisingly unforgiving, and if you upset the juniors, their parents often follow. You can end up in the dog house for no good reason. People can be very unjust.

Juniors however, are usually a good bet for playing games. They tend to like the same sort of things that dogs like and there can be lots of running around and making a noise with high levels of excitement. They'll often let you do things that the adults of the family wouldn't approve of, although you do need to make sure you safeguard yourself and your doggy dignity against anything too extreme. Most dogs are not keen on dressing up clothes, although I do try and be tolerant up to a certain point. 'Her Indoors' reckons it's one of the reasons why, as a senior, I'm very obliging at getting into harnesses and coats. I also have a limited liking for being given rides in things like doll's prams, wheel barrows and sledges. This is an easy one to resolve; you just jump out. Whilst other dogs may have a different view, I'm also not keen on water pistols as I don't like getting wet, so at the first sign I head into the kitchen. In fairness, 'Her Indoors' usually defends my right not to be squirted as she's not keen on that treatment herself, but 'Junior Him' could be quite bold at times, and wasn't entirely to be trusted. It is something, that with careful training, they grow out of in time, so persist with the evasive action and they'll eventually take the hint. However good natured us dogs naturally are, we need to draw the line somewhere and it's important to be consistent with your boundaries so that everyone knows where they stand.

'Him Indoors' has, perhaps surprisingly, responded quite well to training in playing ball with me. He actually has quite a soft heart, which was what allowed me to sneak in under the radar in the first place, and he finds it difficult to ignore my appealing eyes, particularly when I use them at full volume. He might grumble about repeatedly throwing the ball for me, but he's usually quite patient and does it for much longer than 'Her Indoors'. It's his weakness for my pleading expression that also makes him the most useful for giving me little food treats. It also helps that he's not the one who has to take me for my annual check-up at the Vet's with the dreaded weigh-in and the polite scolding if I'm over-weight. After all, I'm only a dog so how could it possibly be my fault if I've gained a little extra to my insulating layer? Anyway, 'Him Indoors' waits until 'Her Indoors' is suitably distracted and then gets my attention with a quick 'Pssst', sneaking me a little morsel of something delicious. I've had all sorts of little treats over the years: cheese, cereal bars, popcorn, roast chicken, gravy, carrot tops, and apple to name just a few. He is also occasionally known to sneak me the last couple of drops of beer from the bottle, something I really enjoy. He holds it upside down and I stick my tongue right up the neck so that none of the precious drops get wasted. 'Her indoors' says I look like a lamb with a bottle, but I don't think the local farmer wastes Peroni on her sheep, although I could be wrong. Anyway, it just shows that even the most unpromising person can be trained by a dog, if they try hard enough, so don't give up on the difficult cases, just see them as a challenge and go for it.

'Him Indoors' always makes excuses for giving me treats on the basis that he's just trying to reduce my life expectancy, but if that is true, and not just a bit of macho bluster to cover the fact that he's been caught doing something vaguely affectionate towards me for a change, it's not working. If I was out sleeping in the sun, when 'Junior Her' was a girl, in that very intense way that we dogs have, he used to annoy her by pretending I was dead and remarking on the quality of my life to date. 'Junior Her' used to put up with this for so long and then used to round on him and tell him in no uncertain terms, what would happen to him if any harm should come to me, and he was then forced to subside. It's not that I haven't got a sense of humour, but you can push a joke too far. One of my Twitter pals said his owner used to refer to him, when he was indulging in in-depth sleeping, as 'road kill' which demonstrates a similar gallows humour. It's always comforting to know, when you are having a particular training issue with your human, that there are others out their similarly afflicted. It can be very helpful to share your experiences so that undesirable behavioural traits can be nipped in the bud, and you can concentrate on having a good time together.

A Final Wag

If you've worked your way doggedly through my advice, you should be well on the way to having a highly-trained family, which will maximise the enjoyment of life for all of you. Whilst 'Them Indoors' are not perfect, I like to think that I've trained them to a higher degree of tolerance, than is normally the case in the human/canine relationship, and I feel a real sense of pride in my achievement.

From the moment I arrived in their lives, I've been at the centre of their universe, which is of course, only right and proper. They have forgiven me my little indiscretions - eventually, although 'Him Indoors' has a worryingly long memory, taken me for innumerable walks, supported me in my various hobbies and ensured that I've lead a varied and full life. They've spent out large sums of money on my private health care, bought me all the latest in doggy accessories and equipment, made me things, fed me the best food and worried about me when I've been ill. And now that I'm a senior fur, they allow me to lead life at my own pace, whilst making sure that I'm still happily participating in whatever life has to offer, which in my case is a considerable amount.

Whilst 'Them Indoors' have stepped up to the mark pretty well, not every human has the circumstances or the capacity to look after a dog for the duration of their entire life, so you need to be aware of this and to be very discerning. There are still far too many dogs, who through no fault of their own, other than an amiable willingness to see the best in people, end up in rescue centres, looking for a new family. I would like to just take a moment to thank the special people who work to try and help these dogs, and the various charities that support them. I know this is a bit partisan of me, but it's my book after all, so a special extra mention goes to Border Terrier Welfare, which does a great job in helping my fellow BTs when they get into difficulties. Take a play bow all of you!

I'd also like to thank all my family and furends, real or virtual, for their continued support. The BT Posse have selflessly aided me in my literary endeavours and have barked about my first book, 'The Last Rolo' to the entire world. Thank you, from the heart of my bottom. I'm indebted, in the advancement of my literary career, to Adele Trathan, Editor of Magnet magazine, for not only giving a senior dog the chance to share his views in a monthly column, but for expanding the size of my column so I've got a bit more space. I might be small, but I've got a bit presence, what can I tell you. Adele also, very charitably in my opinion, gave 'Her Indoors' her own column, which is nowhere near as good as mine. She writes it under the pseudonym 'Paula Menso' (it's an anagram – work it out!), but why she doesn't write under her own name like I do is beyond me.

And finally, I'd like to end with a serious tail wag of celebration, for all the fun and pleasure that the human/dog relationship brings to the world. We are a varied bunch, and so are people, but we were made to be together. Border Terriers are probably not the easiest breed of dog to own, or is that just me? We're independent spirits with a mind of our own, but we're small, generally healthy, hardy and above all fun. And that, my friends, is what it's all about!

About the Author

Rolo Stockton has been the subject of numorous articles for national dog magazines, blogs at www.rolotheborderterrier.blogspot.com, tweets as @stockton_rolo, can be found on Facebook, loitering with intent, @RolotheBorderTerrier, and is a regular colunist, writing *It's a Dog's Life,* for Magnet magazine.

Helen Stockton is Rolo's owner and he's taught her everything she knows about writing! She's a writer and creative writing teacher, www.helenstockton.co.uk. She has written two book, *Teaching Creative Writing,* published by How To Books and *English Language and Literature Reading Skills* published by Pearson Education. She trains creative writing teachers and is a writing mentor and writing for well-being practioner. She writes for a variety of national and local magazines and newspapers, writing a regular column, *And Another Thing…* for Magnet magazine. She tweets @stocktonwriting and is on Facebook @WritingFourLife.